EntreCultures 1A

Communicate, Explore, and Connect Across Cultures

Elizabeth Zwanziger
Hélène Schuster
Brittany Goings
Ed Weiss

Wayside®
PUBLISHING

ENTRECULTURES 1A

Copyright © 2020 by Wayside Publishing

Printed in the USA

1 2 3 4 5 6 7 8 9 10 KP 19

Print date: 1088

Hardcover ISBN 978-1-944876-91-3

Le Monde Francophone

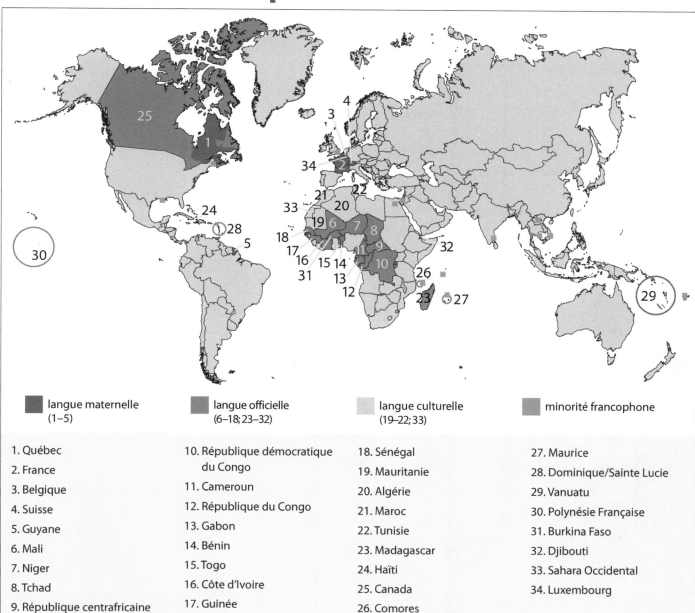

langue maternelle (1–5)

langue officielle (6–18; 23–32)

langue culturelle (19–22; 33)

minorité francophone

1. Québec
2. France
3. Belgique
4. Suisse
5. Guyane
6. Mali
7. Niger
8. Tchad
9. République centrafricaine
10. République démocratique du Congo
11. Cameroun
12. République du Congo
13. Gabon
14. Bénin
15. Togo
16. Côte d'Ivoire
17. Guinée
18. Sénégal
19. Mauritanie
20. Algérie
21. Maroc
22. Tunisie
23. Madagascar
24. Haïti
25. Canada
26. Comores
27. Maurice
28. Dominique/Sainte Lucie
29. Vanuatu
30. Polynésie Française
31. Burkina Faso
32. Djibouti
33. Sahara Occidental
34. Luxembourg

Marc Degioanni - Conseiller pédagogique - Digne (2012), "Monde 4 Francophonie", Retrieved from http://formation.ekladrog.fr/le-monde-seance-n-4-les-pays-francophones-a40996532.

EntreCultures 1A

Glossary of Classroom and Activity Instructions

Expressions pour la salle de classe

asseyez-vous	*sit down*
écoutez	*listen*
fermez vos livres	*close your books*
il vous faut...	*you need...*
levez la main	*raise your hand*
levez-vous	*stand up*
ouvrez vos livres	*open your books*
parlez avec votre voisin	*talk to your neighbor*
parlez en français	*speak French*
regardez-moi	*look at me*
répétez	*repeat*
retournez à vos places	*return to your places*

Expressions de politesse

à vos souhaits	*bless you (after a sneeze)*
excusez-moi	*excuse me*
de rien	*you're welcome*
merci	*thank you*
pardon	*pardon*
s'il vous plaît	*please*

Descriptions d'emplacement

sur

sous

dans

devant

derrière

à côté de

à droite de

à gauche de

loin de

près de

Expressions pour les activités

cherchez	look for	**participez**	participate
choisissez	choose	**pensez**	think
classez	classify	**préparez**	prepare
comparez	compare	**présentez**	present
complétez	complete	**regardez**	watch
créez	create	**répondez**	respond, answer
décrivez	describe	**résumez**	summarize
demandez	ask	**tchattez**	chat (online)
discutez	discuss	**trouvez**	find
échangez	exchange	**utilisez**	use
écoutez	listen		
enregistrez	record, film	**un/une autre élève de classe**	classmate
étudiez	study	**un exemple**	example
expliquez	explain	**une image**	image
identifiez	identify	**un/une partenaire**	partner
indiquez	indicate	**une phrase**	sentence
lisez	read	**une question**	question
mettez	put	**une réponse**	answer
organisez	organize	**un rôle**	role
parlez	talk, speak	**un tableau**	table, chart

Acknowledgements

We extend our sincere gratitude and appreciation to all who accompanied us on our journey from the conception to the completion of this edition of the *EntreCultures* program. We had the privilege to work with a talented and hard-working professional team that served as our anchor during the entire creative process.

From the very beginning of this project, Eliz Tchakarian, Editorial Project Manager, and Janet Parker, Curriculum Coordinator, were dedicated partners who coached us through every step of the journey and consistently helped us pull all of the pieces together in order to create this book. We also greatly appreciate Curriculum Coordinator Helen Small's and Editorial Project Manager Lindsey Colling's guidance in completing the program in its last stage. Kelsey Hare and Elizabeth Rench (Permissions Coordinators) were instrumental and persistent with acquiring permissions for authentic materials. We commend our outstanding editors, Eileen M. Angelini and Ana-Maria M'Enesti, whose advice and editing were indispensible to the completion of this work. Contributing Authors Julia Thornton and Nitya Viswanath enriched the content of our online presence. Our book would not have been as truly authentic nor as engaging without the generous contribution of our international video bloggers, incredible young people from across the Francophone world who shared their lives with our readers to help make a true connection to the French language =and culture. Thanks so much to Marianne, François, Hamid, Jeanne, Ariane, Kate, and Noah for being the faces of *EntreCultures* level one.

We thank Derrick Alderman and Rivka Levin at Bookwonders—our talented and artistic production team—who brought our manuscripts to life on the engaging and colorful pages of the completed product. We thank Wayside Publishing Graphic Designers Nathan Galvez, Sawyer McCarron-Rutledge, Tawny Cantor, and cover designer Shelby Newsted, who designed many of the beautiful graphics and graphic organizers used in both the print and online versions of this book. We extend our appreciation to Senior Tech Support Representatives Maddie Bonneau, James LeVasseur, and everyone else on the IT team led by Manager Deb Penham.

The Wayside Publishing Sales and Marketing team was led by Director Michelle Sherwood, who was assisted by Marketing Manager Nicole Lyons, Professional Development Manager Jay Ketner, and the entire Instructional Strategist team. We'd like to specifically thank all Instructional Strategists, as well as the Marketing Specialists Stefanie Millette and Zsofia McMullin. In collaboration with the Wayside Publishing Sales and Marketing team, we are getting the word out to the French teaching community about *EntreCultures*, a new instructional tool and innovative approach to developing students' intercultural communicative competence.

Finally, we sincerely thank Wayside Publishing President Greg Greuel and Manager of Product Development Steve Whitworth for supporting this project with their clear vision and leadership.

Elizabeth Zwanziger   *Hélène Schuster*   *Brittany Goings*   *Ed Weiss*

World-Readiness Standards For Learning Languages

GOAL AREAS	STANDARDS		
COMMUNICATION Communicate effectively in more than one language in order to function in a variety of situations and for multiple purposes	**Interpersonal Communication:** Learners interact and negotiate meaning in spoken, signed, or written conversations to share information, reactions, feelings, and opinions.	**Interpretive Communication:** Learners understand, interpret, and analyze what is heard, read, or viewed on a variety of topics.	**Presentational Communication:** Learners present information, concepts, and ideas to inform, explain, persuade, and narrate on a variety of topics using appropriate media and adapting to various audiences of listeners, readers, or viewers.
CULTURES Interact with cultural competence and understanding	**Relating Cultural Practices to Perspectives:** Learners use the language to investigate, explain, and reflect on the relationship between the practices and perspectives of the cultures studied.	**Relating Cultural Products to Perspectives:** Learners use the language to investigate, explain, and reflect on the relationship between the products and perspectives of the cultures studied.	
CONNECTIONS Connect with other disciplines and acquire information and diverse perspectives in order to use the language to function in academic and careerrelated situations	**Making Connections:** Learners build, reinforce, and expand their knowledge of other disciplines while using the language to develop critical thinking and to solve problems creatively.	**Acquiring Information and Diverse Perspectives:** Learners access and evaluate information and diverse perspectives that are available through the language and its cultures.	
COMPARISONS Develop insight into the nature of language and culture in order to interact with cultural competence	**Language Comparisons:** Learners use the language to investigate, explain, and reflect on the nature of language through comparisons of the language studied and their own.	**Cultural Comparisons:** Learners use the language to investigate, explain, and reflect on the concept of culture through comparisons of the cultures studied and their own.	
COMMUNITIES Communicate and interact with cultural competence in order to participate in multilingual communities at home and around the world	**School and Global Communities:** Learners use the language both within and beyond the classroom to interact and collaborate in their community and the globalized world.	**Lifelong Learning:** Learners set goals and reflect on their progress in using languages for enjoyment, enrichment, and advancement.	

The National Standards Collaborative Board. (2015). *World-Readiness Standards for Learning Languages*. 4th ed. Alexandria, VA: Author.

Essential Features

Learners maintain an online *Mon dossier* to self-assess, reflect, and upload evidence for each Can-Do statement displayed alongside activities in the Student Edition. Building their collections of artifacts allows learners to form vital habits leading them to efficiently continue learning beyond the classroom.

SELF-ASSESSMENT

INTERCULTURALITY INTERCU

Interculturality is at the heart of EntreCultures

With *EntreCultures*, learners explore and compare Francophone communities to their own communities. Video blogs created by native speakers allow learners to compare their lives with those of their peers. Activities and assessments are based on authentic sources and set in real-life thematic and cultural contexts.

AUTHENTICITY

PERFORMANCE-BASED ASSESSMENT

Units include performance-based formative assessments, *J'avance*, which solidify culturally appropriate communication skills relating to learners' communities. *J'y arrive*, summative integrated performance assessments, engage learners in global intercultural contexts. Analytic rubrics that include intercultural and communicative learning targets accompany summative assessments.

Our vision is a world where language learning takes place through the lens of interculturality, so students can discover appropriate ways to interact with others whose perspectives may be different from their own.

RESOURCES FOR TEACHERS AND STUDENTS

The online **Explorer** provides all audio/video resources; scaffolding for Student Edition activities; vocabulary and grammar reinforcement, including flipped classroom videos; additional activities; formative and summative assessments; rubrics; and other teacher resources.

Appendices

In the Teacher Edition, you are provided with audio and audiovisual transcripts for authentic resources, answer keys, instructional strategies, Can-Do statements for each unit, and rubrics. Indices include a Grammar and Learning Strategies Videos Index as well as an index of grammatical concepts. All glossaries are also included in the program.

EntreCultures Mission and Vision

EntreCultures is a three-level, standards-based, thematically-organized program consisting of six in-depth units per level that provide learners with opportunities to interact and engage with authentic materials and adolescent speakers of the language. By learning in an intercultural context, students acquire communication skills and content knowledge while exploring the products, practices, and perspectives of French-speaking cultures.

EntreCultures Mission

EntreCultures aims to prepare learners to communicate, explore, and connect across cultures in order to foster attitudes of mutual understanding and respect.

EntreCultures Vision

Our vision is a world where language learning takes place through the lens of interculturality, so students can discover appropriate ways to interact with others whose perspectives may be different from their own.

Welcome to *EntreCultures 1A*

Dear students,

Bienvenue à *EntreCultures*!

In today's world, we all live *entre cultures*: that is, we all live around and among people and influences from a variety of cultures. As we live, learn, work and play in our communities and abroad, we interact in person and online with people whose experiences and perspectives may be different from our own.

The learning materials in the *EntreCultures* program were designed to help you communicate in French, and to develop the attitudes and habits of mind to interact appropriately with French speakers, respecting differences and recognizing the many things we share as human beings.

Thank you for the commitment you have made to learning another language. The opportunity to experience interactions across cultures and connect with diverse people in our communities and around the world has brought each of us great personal and professional satisfaction. We hope that through this program you too will embrace the opportunities that will come to you as you live *entre cultures*.

Sincerely,

Elizabeth Zwanziger

Hélène Schuster

Brittany Goings

Ed Weiss

Les Anses-d'Arlet, Martinique

Unit Organization

Rencontre interculturelle

Comment dit-on? 1
Expressions utiles
On peut aussi dire

Découvrons 1
○ **Zoom culture**
Connexions
Réflexions

○ **Réflexion interculturelle**

○ **Mon progrès**
Communicatif
Interculturel

J'avance 1

Comment dit-on? 2
On peut aussi dire
Expressions utiles

Découvrons 2
○ **Zoom culture**
Connexions
Réflexions

○ **Réflexion interculturelle**

○ **Mon progrès**
Communicatif
Interculturel

J'avance 2

Comment dit-on? 3
On peut aussi dire
Expressions utiles

Découvrons 3
○ **Zoom culture**
Connexions
Réflexions

○ **Réflexion interculturelle**

○ **Mon progrès**
Communicatif
Interculturel

J'avance 3

Éléments supplémentaires

Prononciation
Détail grammatical
Détail linguistique
Rappel
Stratégies

J'y arrive!

Introduction to a Unit

Explorer

EntreCultures 1A Explorer resources include video blogs, audio/video authentic resources, vocabulary, grammar and learning strategies videos, additional vocabulary practice, discussion forums, and more. You will collect evidence of growth in **Mon dossier** in Explorer, as well.

Objectifs de l'unité
Review learning targets for interpretive, interpersonal, and presentational communication as well as intercultural learning.

Questions essentielles
Connect day-to-day learning to bigger questions.

Rencontre interculturelle
Start with interculturality.

Communiquons
Integrate language and culture to communicate.

UNITÉ 1
L'identité

Objectifs de l'unité
Interact to express your identity, ask for and give personal information, and express preferences about activities.

Interpret images, video, and audio, and print texts in French to gain insights into identity.

Present basic information about yourself.

Investigate, explain and reflect on the role of language in shaping identity in France, Quebec, and in your community.

40

Questions essentielles
Who am I? How does what I do define who I am?

How do I exchange information about my identity and that of others?

What are cultural similarities and differences between myself and others in a Francophone community?

There are many sides to our identity. We may be students, athletes, artists and volunteers. In this unit, you will learn to talk with French speakers about who you are and start to develop another aspect of your identity: bilingual communicator connecting across cultures.

Rencontre interculturelle 42
Meet Marianne and François through their video blogs. As you **watch** and **listen**, you will learn about their identities and their countries of origin.

Communiquons 46

Comment dit-on? 1: Qui suis-je? 46
Are you an artist? An athlete? A student? **Learn to ask and answer questions** to share information about your identity with French speakers.

Découvrons 1: Expressing Who I Am 52
Learn how to **express your identity and ask about the identity of your classmates.**

J'avance 1 Formative Assessment 55
Assess your progress. **Ask and answer questions about your identity and that of others.**

Comment dit-on? 2: Mes activités préférées 56
Learn to ask about and express some preferences by saying what you like and do not like to do.

Découvrons 2: Expressing Preferences 60
Learn how to **express your preferences and find out about those of your classmates.**

J'avance 2 Formative Assessment
Assess your progress. **Introduce yourself and talk about what you like and don't like to do.**

Comment dit-on? 3: Questions et réponses 69
Learn to exchange additional information about age, origin, personal interests, and which languages you speak. **Identify information** in an advertisement for the **Festival d'été de Québec** about musicians and their identities.

Découvrons 3: Asking and Answering Questions 74
Learn how to **ask and answer questions** in different ways to get to know someone.

J'avance 3 Formative Assessment 80
Assess your progress. **Understand what you hear about others to identify preferences.**

Synthèse de grammaire et vocabulaire 82
Learn to express identity (être), state preferences about activities you like and dislike (*j'aime/tu aimes + infinitive*), and **ask and answer questions.**

J'y arrive 86
Show how well you communicate with young people from a Francophone culture. First, **watch** two students introduce themselves in their video blogs. Then, **respond** to one of them with a simple email. Finally, **prepare** your own video blog to introduce yourself.

UNITÉ 1 41

Comment dit-on?
Begin with the essential vocabulary chunks.

J'avance Formative Assessments
Check progress after each unit section.

Synthèse de grammaire et vocabulaire
Review the language needed.

J'y arrive
Apply learning in the final assessment.

Rencontre interculturelle/Interculturality

Rencontre interculturelle

You will be introduced to the Francophone world with the assistance of our teen video bloggers.

Blogger videos are available in Explorer.

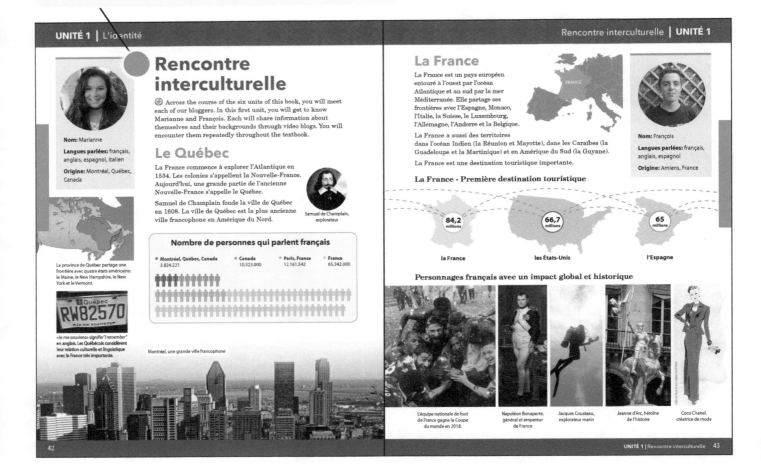

UNITÉ 1 | L'identité

Rencontre interculturelle

Across the course of the six units of this book, you will meet each of our bloggers. In this first unit, you will get to know Marianne and François. Each will share information about themselves and their backgrounds through video blogs. You will encounter them repeatedly throughout the textbook.

Nom: Marianne

Langues parlées: français, anglais, espagnol, italien

Origine: Montréal, Québec, Canada

Le Québec

La France commence à explorer l'Atlantique en 1534. Les colonies s'appellent la Nouvelle-France. Aujourd'hui, une grande partie de l'ancienne Nouvelle-France s'appelle le Québec.

Samuel de Champlain fonde la ville de Québec en 1608. La ville de Québec est la plus ancienne ville francophone en Amérique du Nord.

Samuel de Champlain, explorateur

La province de Québec partage une frontière avec quatre états américains: le Maine, le New Hampshire, le New York et le Vermont.

RW82570 — Québec — Je me souviens

«Je me souviens» signifie "I remember" en anglais. Les Québécois considèrent leur relation culturelle et linguistique avec la France très importante.

Nombre de personnes qui parlent français

Montréal, Québec, Canada	Canada	Paris, France	France
3.824.221	10.523.000	12.161.542	65.342.000

Montréal, une grande ville francophone

Rencontre interculturelle | UNITÉ 1

La France

La France est un pays européen entouré à l'ouest par l'océan Atlantique et au sud par la mer Méditerranée. Elle partage ses frontières avec l'Espagne, Monaco, l'Italie, la Suisse, le Luxembourg, l'Allemagne, l'Andorre et la Belgique.

La France a aussi des territoires dans l'océan Indien (la Réunion et Mayotte), dans les Caraïbes (la Guadeloupe et la Martinique) et en Amérique du Sud (la Guyane).

La France est une destination touristique importante.

FRANCE

Nom: François

Langues parlées: français, anglais, espagnol

Origine: Amiens, France

La France - Première destination touristique

84,2 millions	66,7 millions	65 millions
la France	les États-Unis	l'Espagne

Personnages français avec un impact global et historique

L'équipe nationale de foot de France gagne la Coupe du monde en 2018.

Napoléon Bonaparte, général et empereur de France

Jacques Cousteau, explorateur marin

Jeanne d'Arc, héroïne de l'histoire

Coco Chanel, créatrice de mode

Rencontre interculturelle | **UNITÉ 1**

Activité 1

Bonjour, Marianne et François!

Record your responses to the following in the discussion forum in Explorer.

📖 🌐 Étape 1: Préparez

Look at the pictures of Marianne and François and what is in their speech bubbles. What kind of information do you think they have included in their video blogs? What do you think the phrases in the speech bubbles mean?

▶️ 🌐 Étape 2: Écoutez

Listen to the video blogs and raise your hand when you think you hear Marianne and François say the words from the picture captions.

▶️ 🌐 Étape 3: Résumez

Listen and watch again. Based on what you see and hear, write two sentences about what you think Marianne and François are telling us in their video blogs.

💬 Étape 4: Comparez

How are Marianne and François similar to you? How are they different? Share your observations in class and in your *EntreCultures 1* Explorer course.

Réflexion interculturelle

💬 🌐 What did you notice in the video about what Marianne and François like and don't like? She likes playing soccer and hanging out with friends and family. He says he likes to skateboard and read comics, but doesn't like doing homework. Are these likes and dislikes similar or different from yours? Do you think playing sports in Quebec is the same as in your school? Do you think homework in France poses the same or different challenges than homework in your school? In preparation for answering the questions in the discussion forum in Explorer, complete the *diagramme de Venn* first.

Le Carnaval d'hiver de Québec

La plus grande cathédrale en France est à Amiens!

Mon progrès interculturel

I can identify some similarities and differences between Francophone young people and myself.

Réflexion interculturelle

After a variety of experiences with cultural products, practices, and perspectives, you will reflect on your growing intercultural awareness.

You will share reflections in an Explorer discussion forum.

Mon progrès interculturel

This unique self-assessment feature makes intercultural goals explicit to you.

You will provide evidence of growth in *Mon dossier* in Explorer.

Zoom culture

Knowing about cultural products, practices, and perspectives lays a foundation for intercultural reflections.

You will share reflections in the Explorer discussion forum.

UNITÉ 1 | L'identité

On peut aussi dire

Qui suis-je?

acteur/actrice
bénévole
blogueur/blogueuse
créateur/créatrice de mode
cycliste
danseur/danseuse
explorateur/exploratrice
inventeur/inventrice
photographe
poète
scientifique

Mon progrès communicatif

I can ask and answer simple questions about identity.

Activité 4

Mon identité et ton identité

📖 🌐 Étape 1: Écrivez

Look at the list of identities in the chart and write *oui* or *non* in the first column (under *moi*) to indicate if they correspond or do not correspond to your identity.

les identités	moi	élève 1	élève 2	élève 3
musicien/ musicienne*				
athlète				
élève				
chanteur/ chanteuse				
artiste				
bilingue				
américain/ américaine				
sérieux/ sérieuse				

*If there are two versions of the word listed, use the first one (*musicien*) for a male and the second one (*musicienne*) for a female.

💬 Étape 2: Demandez

Ask questions to three of your classmates, following this pattern, and record their answers in the chart in *Étape 1*.

Modèle

Élève A: Es-tu musicien(ne)?
Élève B: Non, je ne suis pas musicien(ne).

Élève A: Es-tu athlète?
Élève B: Oui, je suis athlète.

48

Vocabulaire

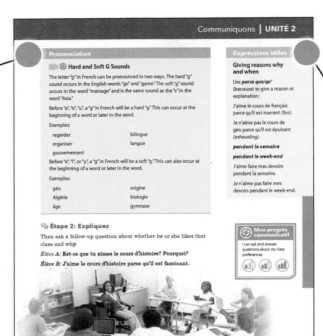

Prononciation

You will learn about sounds that occur in French and listen to them being modeled by a native speaker.

Pronunciation videos are available in Explorer.

Expressions utiles

These quick reminders show how expressions can boost communication skills, often with phrases that will work across other themes.

Comment dit-on?

Essential vocabulary is presented visually in manageable chunks and authentic contexts.

On peut aussi dire

Additional vocabulary provides personalization, extension, and variation of skills.

For every vocabulary section, there are *activités supplémentaires* in Explorer which provide extra practice, if needed or desired. You do not need to complete all of these activities to be successful on *J'avance* or *J'y arrive* assessments.

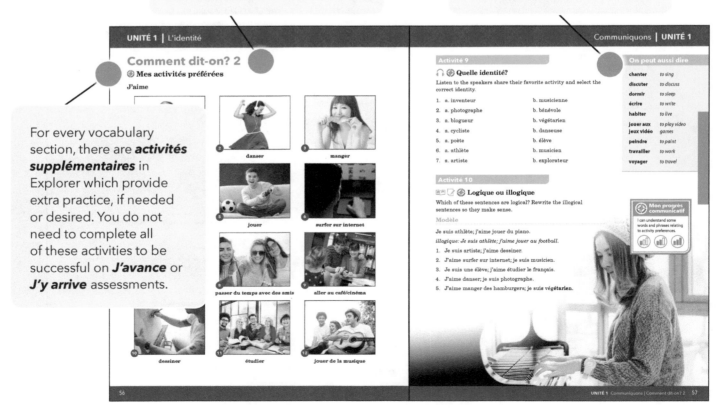

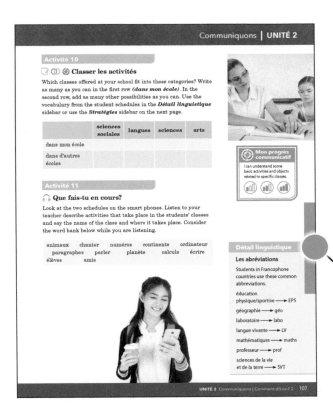

Détail linguistique

You will explore curious and useful details of the language.

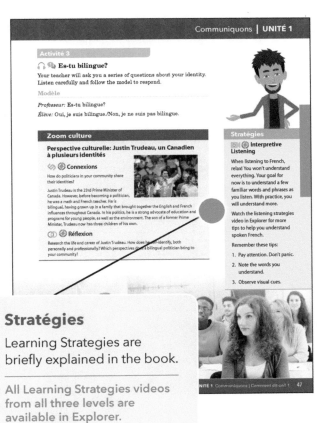

Stratégies

Learning Strategies are briefly explained in the book.

All Learning Strategies videos from all three levels are available in Explorer.

Vocabulaire

These lists summarize the vocabulary studied in the unit.

You will find more practice in context in Explorer.

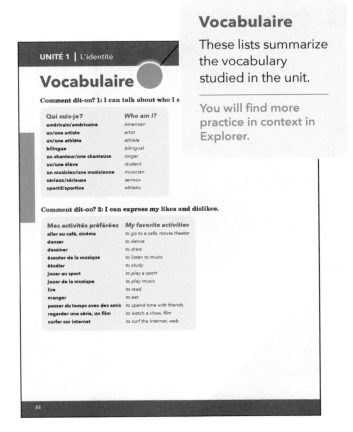

Grammaire

Découvrons

Examples of new structures in context encourage you to become "grammar detectives."

You will find helpful videos called *Découvrons* and *Structure en avant* in Explorer.

UNITÉ 1 | L'identité

Découvrons 1
Expressing Who I Am

Je parle français et espagnol. Et toi, tu es bilingue?

Oui, moi aussi. Je suis bilingue. Je parle français et italien.

Découvertes

Read the dialogue above and notice the words in bold used to introduce identities (**es, suis**). What do you observe about the different forms? Can you figure out when to use **es** and **suis**? Discuss with classmates and teacher, view the *Découvrons 1* resources for this unit in your Explorer course, and check the *Synthèse de grammaire* at the end of this unit.

52

For every grammar section, there are *activités supplémentaires* in Explorer which provide extra practice, if needed or desired.

Synthèse de grammaire

This summary contains helpful explanations of grammatical structures.

You will find more practice in context in Explorer.

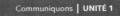

Étape 1: Écrivez

Look at these words. Select and write five words that describe your identity. Don't let anyone else see your words!

Noms	Adjectifs
acteur/actrice	actif/active
artiste	ambitieux/ambitieuse
chanteur/chanteuse	courageux/courageuse
créateur/créatrice de mode	sérieux/sérieuse
cycliste	sportif/sportive
élève	timide
photographe	

Étape 2: Demandez et répondez

Working with a *partenaire*, ask questions like the ones in the model until your *partenaire* answers affirmatively based on his or her list from *Étape 1*. Then switch roles. **Note**: Read the *Détail grammatical* concerning the verb *être* to help you use complete sentences in your answer.

Modèle

Tu es sportif/sportive?

Est-ce que tu es chanteur/chanteuse?

Détail grammatical

Le verbe être

The verb *être* is the most commonly used verb in French and is one way to express identity.

je suis	*I am*
tu es	*you (familiar/informal); are*
elle est	*she is*
il est	*he is*

To make the above forms negative, surround the verb form with the words **ne... pas**:

je**ne** suis **pas**
tu**n'**es **pas**
il/elle **n'**est **pas**

Détail grammatical

Timely grammar details will help you communicate.

UNITÉ 1 Communiquons | Découvrons 1   53

UNITÉ 1 | L'identité

Synthèse de grammaire

1. Expressing Who I am: *le verbe être et les adjectifs*

In this unit, you have seen three forms of the verb *être* (to be); all the present tense forms of this verb are given below:

	singular one person		plural two or more persons	
the speaker **him or herself**	je	suis	nous	sommes
the person spoken **to**	tu *(informal)*	es	vous *(formal or informal)*	êtes
	vous *(formal)**	êtes		
the person or people spoken **about**	il	est	ils	sont
	elle	est	elles	sont

*The versatile subject pronoun **vous** may refer to either one person or any number of people since it can be found in both the singular and plural columns in the chart above. **Vous**, when referring to a singular person, has a formal tone as opposed to the word **tu**, which is used to reference someone informally, like a brother, sister or good friend. Use **vous** to refer to a teacher or an adult neighbor. For future reference, when you encounter a verb conjugation chart like the one above, **vous** will be located only on the plural side of those charts, no matter if it would be plural or singular, formal or informal.

The verb *être* can be used with adjectives to describe a person's identity:

— **Tristan est sérieux.**

Tristan is serious.

— **Carole est sérieuse.**

Carole is serious.

82

Évaluations

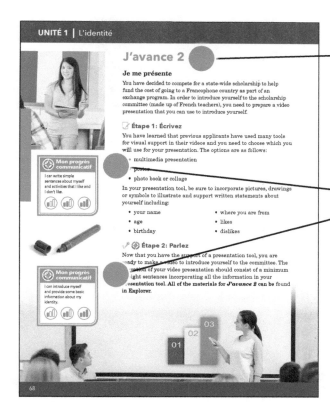

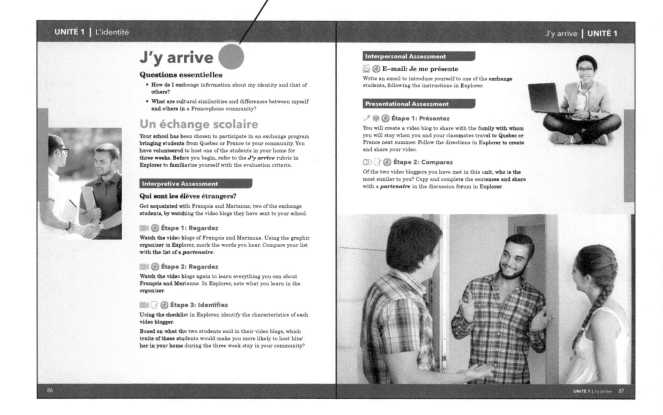

J'avance

Formative assessments measure your progress towards unit goals.

Find supporting materials in Explorer.

Mon progrès communicatif

You will provide evidence of growing proficiency in ***Mon dossier***, which contains all Can-Do statements included throughout the unit.

J'y arrive

A final assessment set in an authentic intercultural context.

Find supporting materials in Explorer.

Explorer®

The online Explorer is the other half of the textbook, connecting students with language learning resources that inspire continued exploration.

Whether learning about Quebec through Marianne's video blogs, studying grammar through flipped classroom videos, or updating language learning portfolios with new achievements, students can practice all modes of communication at their own pace and within their own comfort zone.

FlexText®

FlexText® is Wayside's unique e-textbook platform. Built in HTML5, our digital textbook technology automatically adjusts the book pages to whatever screen you are using for optimal viewing.

Your FlexText® can be accessed across all of your devices. And page by page, just like the printed textbook, FlexText® allows students and teachers to use **EntreCultures** on the go.

Icons Legend

The icons in this program:

- Indicate the mode of communication
- Reference the five goal areas as listed in the *World-Readiness Standards for Learning Languages*
- Provide a signpost where Explorer offers more support
- Prepare teachers and learners for the type of each task/activity

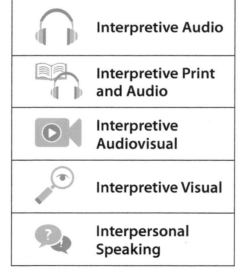

⊙⊙ Linguistic or cultural comparisons	🎧 Interpretive Audio	📋 Interpersonal Writing
🧲 Connections	📖🎧 Interpretive Print and Audio	🎤 Presentational Speaking
👥 Communities	▶️📹 Interpretive Audiovisual	✍️ Presentational Writing
🌐 Cultures	🔍 Interpretive Visual	🧭 Explorer
📖 Interpretive Print	💬 Interpersonal Speaking	

Scavenger Hunt

This scavenger hunt is designed to give you an opportunity to explore the different helpful and interesting features of your **EntreCultures 1A** text and online Explorer.

What food is featured on the cover? Investigate the origin of this French favorite.	Identify the focus of the first **Zoom culture** in Unit 2.	Find the **Expressions utiles** in Unit 1, **Découvrons 2**. Try your best to pronounce the expressions in French. Write down your favorite one.	What country is the focus of the **Rencontre interculturelle** in Unit 2?
Using the table of contents, identify on which page you can find the **Comment dit-on? 1** section of Unit 3.	From what countries are the two video bloggers from Unit 1?	What do the icons before **Activité 6** in Unit 3 indicate to you? Where did you find your answer?	Find three famous Francophone people in the preliminary Unit. Who surprised you and why?
In Explorer, find the forum for this **Réflexion interculturelle** in Unit 2 and post a video.	Identify a **Mon progrès communicatif** in Unit 1. To what activity does it correspond?	In which unit will you learn to communicate about your favorite school subjects?	How many **Découvrons** are there in each unit?
Find an image you like and research to learn something new about the person or location pictured.	Who is the video blogger for Unit 3? Find and watch the video in Explorer.	In Explorer, find the **Découvrons 1** video for Unit 2. What is the topic?	Find the **Stratégies** sidebar in Unit 2. What is the title? Head to Explorer to watch the video.

Objectifs de l'unité

Interact in French, asking and answering some basic questions to meet and get to know others.

Interpret charts, graphs, and images to learn about diverse places, people, and cultures where French is spoken.

Reflect on how to communicate and interact respectfully when meeting people from other cultures.

Questions essentielles

How widely is French used in the world, on the Internet, and in my community?

How do I begin and maintain a simple conversation when meeting a French speaker?

What strategies will help me communicate in French as I begin to learn the language?

Unité preliminaire: Bonjour!

Unité 1: L'identité

Objectifs de l'unité

Interact to express your identity, ask for and give personal information, and express preferences about activities.

Interpret images, video, and audio, and print texts in French to gain insights into identity.

Present basic information about yourself.

Investigate, explain and reflect on the role of language in shaping identity in France, Quebec, and in your community.

Questions essentielles

Who am I? How does what I do define who I am?

How do I exchange information about my identity and that of others?

What are cultural similarities and differences between myself and others in a Francophone community?

Objectifs de l'unité

Exchange information about your life at school, including people, places, schedules, and student activities.

Interpret images, videos, and schedules to gain insights into what school life is like in a Francophone country.

Present information about your own life at school.

Investigate elements of school life and aspects of time in Francophone cultures.

Questions essentielles

How is student life at my school similar to and/or different from student life in a Francophone country?

How do courses and schedules reflect the educational values of a community?

What places, people, and activities define student life?

Unité 2: À l'école

Unité 3: La vie en famille

Objectifs de l'unité

Exchange information about family and home life.

Interpret print texts, infographics, charts, graphs, audios, and videos about family life and activities.

Present a collection of images to share information about a home, a family and/or friends.

Explore family life in Francophone cultures.

Questions essentielles

Who are the members of a family?

Which attributes and interests do family members share?

Which places and activities bring families together in our culture and in Francophone cultures?

Provence, France

Bienvenue!

🎧 ✳ In today's world, we all live *entre cultures*. Through technology and face-to-face communication, we can interact with people with different cultural backgrounds every day. As you use *EntreCultures*, you will learn to speak French and you will explore the cultures of the **Francophone** (French-speaking) world. Everything you learn will help you interact appropriately and respectfully with people whose experiences and perspectives may differ from your own.

Montmartre, France

Canada

États-Un

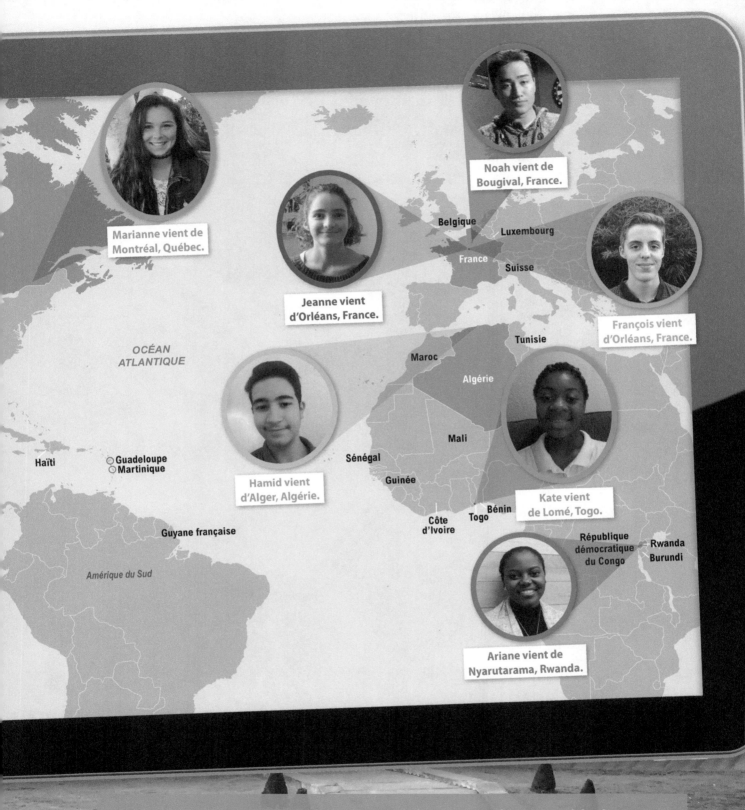

Marianne vient de Montréal, Québec.

Noah vient de Bougival, France.

Jeanne vient d'Orléans, France.

François vient d'Orléans, France.

Hamid vient d'Alger, Algérie.

Kate vient de Lomé, Togo.

Ariane vient de Nyarutarama, Rwanda.

OCÉAN ATLANTIQUE

Haïti

Guadeloupe
Martinique

Guyane française

Amérique du Sud

Belgique

Luxembourg

France

Suisse

Tunisie

Maroc

Algérie

Mali

Sénégal

Guinée

Côte d'Ivoire

Togo

Bénin

République démocratique du Congo

Rwanda

Burundi

Meet seven young people from around the Francophone world who are inviting you to join them in living *EntreCultures*. Listen to them introduce themselves, then locate their countries on the map.

UNITÉ PRÉLIMINAIRE
Bonjour!

Objectifs de l'unité

Interact in French, asking and answering some basic questions to meet and get to know others.

Interpret charts, graphs, and images to learn about diverse places, people, and cultures where French is spoken.

Reflect on how to communicate and interact respectfully when meeting people from other cultures.

✪ Questions essentielles

How widely is French used in the world, on the Internet, and in my community?

How do I begin and maintain a simple conversation when meeting a French speaker?

What strategies will help me communicate in French as I begin to learn the language?

Activité 1

📖 ⦾ Parlez-vous français?

The French language is one of the most important languages in today's world and has contributed to the richness of the English language. Each of the expressions on the image are French words found in an English-language dictionary. The bottom line: the French language has contributed thousands of words to English.

limousine/ chauffeur

café

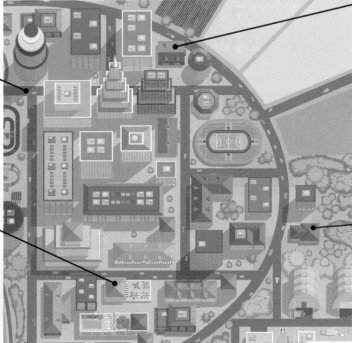

RSVP

RSVP

ballet

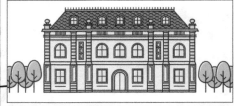

château

While looking at the image of the town, select the French terms from the image that match the descriptions. Let's see how many you can identify!

1. The person who drives the extra-long vehicle.
2. The locale where classic dancing is performed.
3. The magnificent home that looks like a castle.
4. The place where you can get a bite to eat and a beverage.
5. The long luxury vehicle.
6. The part of the meal that comes first; an appetizer.
7. The long crusty loaf of bread.
8. The tasty "pie" made of eggs and cheese.
9. The crescent shaped, flaky roll often enjoyed at breakfast.
10. The oblong pastry filled with cream and topped with chocolate.

CAFÉ MENU
À la carte
Hors d'oeuvre
Baguette
Croissant
Omelette
Quiche
Éclair

Le français dans le monde

What can you learn from these graphics about French in today's world?

📖 ✛ Étape 1 : Regardez

Scan the chart *Les dix langues les plus parlées sur internet* and answer the following questions.

1. Which do you think is ranked on this chart: countries or languages? Why?

2. Is French represented? What are the clues?

📖 ✛ Read the chart a second time and answer the following questions.

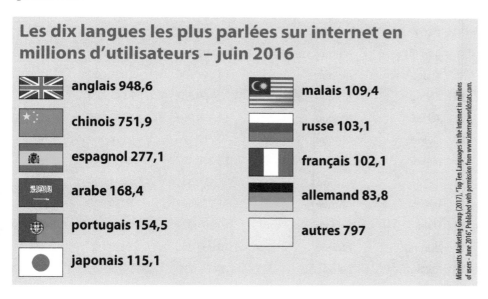

Les dix langues les plus parlées sur internet en millions d'utilisateurs – juin 2016

anglais 948,6

chinois 751,9

espagnol 277,1

arabe 168,4

portugais 154,5

japonais 115,1

malais 109,4

russe 103,1

français 102,1

allemand 83,8

autres 797

Miniwatts Marketing Group (2017), "Top Ten Languages in the Internet in millions of users – June 2016." Published with permission from www.internetworldstats.com.

3. What does this infographic show us?

4. Where does French rank in this chart?

5. What do the numbers represent?

6. Which of the languages listed are official languages of countries in North America?

Kinshasa, République démocratique du Congo

Étape 2: Lisez

French is the fifth most widely-spoken language in the world, with 274,000,000 speakers. You are among 125,000,000 students who are learning French.

Scan the chart ***Pays ayant le français comme langue officielle*** and answer the questions.

Pays ayant le français comme langue officielle

	pays	continent	population (est. 2017)	francophones (est. 2016)	%
1	Congo (RDC)	Afrique	81 339 988	37 175 000	47 %
2	France	Europe	67 614 002	65 342 000	96 %
3	Canada	Amérique du Nord	36 624 199	10 523 000	29 %
4	Madagascar	Afrique	25 570 895	4 983 000	20 %
5	Côte d'Ivoire	Afrique	24 294 750	7 881 000	34 %
6	Cameroun	Afrique	24 053 727	9 546 000	40 %
7	Niger	Afrique	21 477 348	2 631 000	13 %
8	Burkina Faso	Afrique	19 193 382	4 124 000	22 %
9	Mali	Afrique	18 541 980	3 061 000	17 %
10	Sénégal	Afrique	15 850 567	4 521 000	29 %
11	Tchad	Afrique	14 899 994	1 827 000	13 %
12	Guinée	Afrique	12 717 176	3 118 000	24 %
13	Rwanda	Afrique	12 208 407	669 000	6 %
14	Belgique	Europe	11 429 336	8 224 000	72 %
15	Bénin	Afrique	11 175 692	3 950 000	35 %
16	Haïti	Amérique du Nord	10 981 229	4 556 000	42 %
17	Burundi	Afrique	10 864 245	959 000	8 %
18	Suisse	Europe	8 476 005	5 494 000	66 %
19	Togo	Afrique	7 797 694	2 914 000	39 %
20	Congo (RC)	Afrique	5 260 750	2 758 000	58 %

1. How are these countries ranked?

2. Which country has the greatest number of French speakers?

3. How many continents are represented in this list?

4. Where is French an official language in North America?

5. Which continent has the most countries with French as an official language?

6. How are the numbers written differently in French?

Pira, Bénin

📖 ✦ Étape 3: Lisez et répondez

Scan the world map and answer the questions.

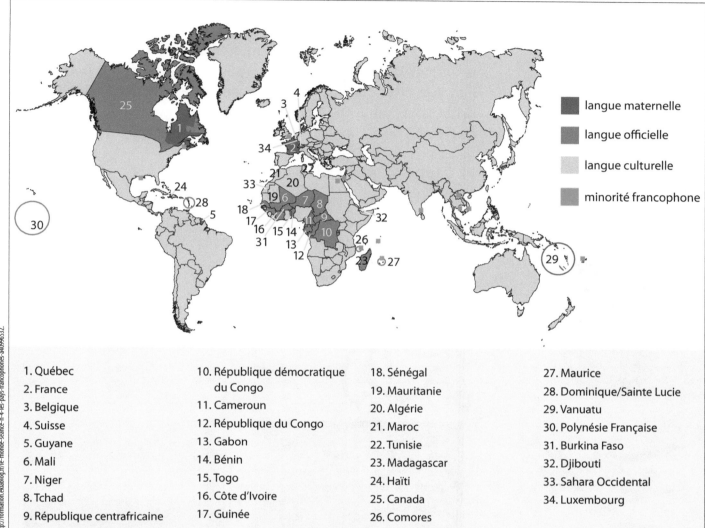

Marc Degioanni - Conseiller pédagogique - Digne (2012), "Monde 4 Francophonie", Retrieved from http://formation.eklablog.fr/le-monde-seance-n-4-les-pays-francophones-a40996532.

Légende:
- langue maternelle
- langue officielle
- langue culturelle
- minorité francophone

1. Québec
2. France
3. Belgique
4. Suisse
5. Guyane
6. Mali
7. Niger
8. Tchad
9. République centrafricaine

10. République démocratique du Congo
11. Cameroun
12. République du Congo
13. Gabon
14. Bénin
15. Togo
16. Côte d'Ivoire
17. Guinée

18. Sénégal
19. Mauritanie
20. Algérie
21. Maroc
22. Tunisie
23. Madagascar
24. Haïti
25. Canada
26. Comores

27. Maurice
28. Dominique/Sainte Lucie
29. Vanuatu
30. Polynésie Française
31. Burkina Faso
32. Djibouti
33. Sahara Occidental
34. Luxembourg

1. On how many continents is French spoken?

2. Approximately how many countries/regions do you see that use French as either an official or governmental (administrative) language?

3. In about how many other countries is there significant French use?

4. Name some places in or near North America where French-language speakers are a significant minority.

5. After having looked at the two previous charts and this map, give two reasons why French is an important world language. Use evidence from the data to support your answer.

✦ Mon progrès communicatif

I can identify and name places on a map where French is spoken around the world.

Activité 3

Connexions francophones

  Étape 1: Pensez

How frequently is French encountered in or near North America or online? How frequently is it encountered online? What are some places or situations in which you could use your developing French skills, now and in the future? Answer these questions in the discussion forum in your *EntreCultures 1* Explorer course.

Étape 2: Regardez et associez

Many French products are known around the world. The following images represent some of the more popular French products and companies. See if you can match the image with the French company.

A

B

C

D

1. Air France
2. Perrier
3. Michelin
4. Lacoste

🔍 📖 ✳ Étape 3: Lisez et associez

Paris (known as ***la ville lumière***, the city of light) is the best-known Francophone city and one of the greatest centers of art, architecture and history on earth. Many of the institutions, museums, and locales of Paris are familiar to people everywhere. See how many of the following Parisian icons you can match with its description.

1. ***La Tour Eiffel*** *(The Eiffel Tower)* - This structure was the tallest building on earth for a quarter of a century.

2. ***Les Champs Élysées*** - One of the best-known streets on earth, it is located in the heart of Paris.

3. ***La Seine*** *(The Seine River)* - It divides Paris into two halves: the right and left banks ***(les rives droites et gauches)***.

4. ***Le Louvre*** *(The Louvre Museum)* - One of the most famous museums in the world, home to ***La Joconde*** *(The Mona Lisa)*, with a glass pyramid entrance.

5. ***Notre Dame de Paris*** *(Notre Dame Cathedral)* Construction began nearly 900 years ago and was the subject of Victor Hugo's novel known in English as <u>The Hunchback of Notre Dame</u>.

6. ***L'Opéra*** *(Paris opera house)* - Known as the ***Palais Garnier***, it is the setting for the novel <u>Phantom of the Opera</u>.

7. ***L'Arc de Triomphe*** *(The Arc of Triumph)* - Built during the Napoleonic era to commemorate military might, this triumphal arch is also the location of the tomb of the unknown soldier.

8. ***Le Penseur*** *(The Thinker)* - This statue by Auguste Rodin is known world-wide.

9. ***Le Centre Pompidou*** *(The Pompidou Center)* - An architectural innovation built during the 1970's, it serves as the museum of modern art.

🎧 ✳ Étape 4: Écoutez

Listen to the names of famous places in Paris and match them with the images in ***Étape 3***.

Réflexion interculturelle

🌐 ✳ Which products and landmarks of the Francophone world are known worldwide? What are some aspects of French life and culture that are revealed via these recognized icons? Answer the questions in the discussion forum in Explorer.

> ✳ **Mon progrès interculturel**
>
> I can identify some familiar products, landmarks, and monuments and what they represent to the Francophone people.

Communiquons
Comment dit-on? 1

🎧 🧭 **Bonjour et au revoir**

Bonjour, comment t'appelles-tu?

Je m'appelle Gabrielle.

Enchanté!

Salut, Mathilde. Comment ça va?

Ça va bien, et toi?

Ça va très bien, merci.

Bonjour, Monsieur. Comment allez-vous?

Très bien, Aurélie. Et toi?

Ça va bien, merci.

D'où viens-tu?

Je viens de Bruxelles.

Ciao!

Au revoir!

À bientôt!

À plus!

Enchanté(e)!

💬 Étape 1: Répondez

To help your teacher take roll, he or she will greet you and ask your name. Answer with your name, using the **modèle** as a guide.

Modèle
....

Professeur: Comment t'appelles-tu?

Élève: Je m'appelle _____.

💬 Étape 2: Demandez et répondez

Greet and ask the name of at least five of your classmates.

Modèle
....

Élève A: Bonjour! Comment t'appelles-tu?

Élève B: Bonjour. Je m'appelle _____.

Élève A: Enchanté(e).

💬 Saluer un(e) ami(e)

Greet five different students in the class. If you don't know their names, add **Comment t'appelles-tu**? If you know their name, simply follow the **modèle**.

Modèle
....

Élève A: Bonjour, _____, comment ça va?

Élève B: Ça va bien, et toi?

Élève A: Ça va très bien, merci.

Activité 6

💬 Bonjour Monsieur/Madame.

Pretend that your classmate is your teacher. Greet your teacher addressing him as **Monsieur** or her as **Madame**, then reverse roles.

Modèle

Élève: Bonjour, Monsieur. Comment allez-vous?

Professeur: Très bien, merci.

Activité 7

💬 Ton origine

Ask and answer the question to find out where at least five other classmates are from. Include your town, city, or state in your answer.

Modèle

Élève A: D'où viens-tu?

Élève B: Je suis de _____.

Activité 8

🎧 ✸ L'origine

Listen to the following people introduce themselves and give their origin. Match the first name that you hear with the place of origin of that person. Note that neither the names nor the origins are in the order in which you will hear them in the recording.

nom	origine
Christelle	Port-au Prince, Haïti
Daniel	Nice, France
Gérard	Abidjan, Côte d'Ivoire
Grace	Antananarivo, Madagascar
Thomas	Québec, Canada
Mendrika	Bruxelles, Belgique

Mon progrès communicatif

I can understand some basic words and phrases when a French speaker introduces him or herself.

Abidjan, Côte d'Ivoire

Activité 9

  Bonjour ou au revoir?

Listen to the following statements and decide whether each one is a *bonjour* (*welcoming greeting*) or an *au revoir* (*goodbye*).

	bonjour	au revoir
1.		
2.		
3.		
4.		
5.		

Uz redzēšanos
Näkemiin ลาก่อน Adiós
مع السلامة До свидания Hoşçakalın
Uz redzēšanos ciao Totsiens Hwyl fawr
Poroporoaki Slán さようなら Viso gero
Arrivederci Goodbye Agur Tchau
Viszontlátásra Tot ziens 再見 Farvel Баяртай
להתראות Au revoir Auf Wiedersehen
Do widzenia 안녕히 가세요 Dovidenia
خداحافظ Tam biêt Збогум 再见
नमस्कार salut Αντίο Ha det bra
Selamat tinggal

Can you find the expression in French for saying "good-bye"?

Zoom culture

Pratique Culturelle: Les salutations et l'espace vital

  Connexions

1. How do people greet each other where you live?

2. What is the typical distance you maintain when speaking to someone your age? Someone older? Someone of a different sex?

3. How does it feel when someone invades your personal space?

In many cultures, it is common to exchange handshakes, hugs, a backslap, or kisses when greeting someone and saying good-bye. In many Francophone countries, friends and family greet each other with kisses on the cheek called *la bise*. The number of kisses and who receives them depends on the region and the gender of the recipient. However, a formal greeting is almost always a handshake no matter the sex, region or social status of the people involved.

French even has different ways of saying "you," depending on the level of formality or social distance and region. *Tu* is used with friends and family, while *vous* is more appropriate for older people or formal settings. You will study these differences in later chapters. For now, it makes sense to observe interactions in the text and online to become familiar with the practices relating to greetings and physical space.

Réflexion

Answer the following question in the discussion forum in Explorer:

1. How do your actions and language change between an informal or formal greeting?

2. Is that similar or different to what you know about the Francophone world?

On peut aussi dire

The **On peut aussi dire** (*you can also say…*) segment will give you additional vocabulary throughout the book to express your ideas in French.

The phrase **Ça va**? (*How are you*? or *How is it going*?) is usually used as a greeting; the answer is almost always **Oui!** (*Yes!*) or **Bien!** (*Well!*), not a true report on how you really are. However, you can give a more accurate answer with the following expressions.

très bien	*very well*
comme ci, comme ça	*so-so, OK*
pas mal	*not bad*
mal	*bad, not well at all*

Mon progrès interculturel

I can identify appropriate expressions and practices, such as gestures and body language, associated with greetings, introductions, and leave-taking in Francophone cultures.

Activité 10

💬 Au revoir!

Practice saying goodbye to classmates. Wave to each classmate as you walk away and vary the expressions you use.

Activité 11

📹🌐✳ La bise

Watch the video in Explorer and discuss your answers with a *partenaire* (*partner*) OR answer the questions in your Explorer course. If you have any questions, be sure to note them and research the answer.

1. How do friends greet each other?
2. How do family members greet each other?
3. How do strangers greet each other?
4. How many kisses are typical in Amiens?
5. What greeting action is used in a formal situation?

Réflexion interculturelle

◑ ✳ Describe how young people in Francophone cultures greet family, friends and teachers.

How is this similar or different from your way of greeting others? How do you feel about greeting your friends and family with a *bise*? Would you be comfortable using the appropriate greetings and good-byes in a Francophone culture? Why or why not? How important is it to adjust your behavior to fit in with another culture?

Provide the information requested and answer the questions in the discussion forum in Explorer.

Activité 12

  Ma première conversation en français!

Combine all the expressions you have learned so far to have a complete conversation. Repeat with at least two classmates. Be sure to practice both A and B roles. Once you've practiced both A and B roles, record your conversation in Explorer with your partner.

Modèle

Élève A: Bonjour! Je m'appelle _____. Comment t'appelles-tu?

Élève B: Je m'appelle _____.

Élève A: Enchanté(e). D'où viens-tu?

Élève B: Je viens de _____.

Élève A: Intéressant! Au revoir!

Élève B: À plus!

Mon progrès communicatif

I can answer questions about my name, how I am, and where I am from.

Mon progrès communicatif

I can ask and answer questions to meet and greet a young person.

Mont Saint-Michel, France

Comment dit-on? 2

▶️ 🧭 **Expressions pour la salle de classe**

The students in the images below are following directions that their teacher gave them. Scan the images, noticing what the students are doing. Can you tell what the teacher must have asked them to do?

1 répétez

2 écoutez

3 parlez français

4 levez la main

5 asseyez-vous

6 levez-vous

7 ouvrez vos livres

8 fermez vos livres

9 parlez avec votre voisin

10 regardez-moi

11 retournez à vos places

12 il vous faut

Mariame: Mariame lives in Geneva, Switzerland. She is 35 and loves to listen to music and sing along.

Océane: Océane lives in a small town in France near the Belgian border. She is 14 and loves to dance and play soccer. She has a little sister named Aurélie who also loves to dance.

Malek: Malek is from Senegal and is living in the capital, Dakar. He is 24 and loves to eat spicy food and travel.

Félix: Félix is from Quebec City and is now living in France. He is 16 and loves to play basketball and hockey.

Activité 13

▶ ✦ Écoutez le professeur!

Watch the video in Explorer, listening closely to what the teacher is asking the students to do and observe how the students react. Can you tell what the teacher must have said to the students? Discuss with classmates and teacher and view the **Comment dit-on? 2** resources at the end of this unit to help you find out.

Activité 14

▶ 📖 ✦ Écoutez et lisez

Watch the video again. When the teacher says a sentence, point to that sentence on the list below.

levez la main	levez-vous	asseyez-vous
ouvrez vos livres	fermez vos livres	sortez vos livres
parlez avec votre voisin	regardez-moi	écoutez
répétez	retournez à vos places	il vous faut…
parlez en français		

Activité 15

▶ ✦ Écoutez et réagissez en cours

Now play the second video in Explorer. When the teacher asks the class to do something, act out what is being asked.

Détail linguistique

S'il vous plaît

S'il vous plaît is an expression that can be added to the beginning or the end of request to make it polite.

Mon progrès communicatif

I can follow classroom commands.

Comment dit-on? 3

✦ Le calendrier: les numéros, les mois et les dates en contexte

janvier 2019

lundi	mardi	mercredi	jeudi	vendredi	samedi	dimanche
	1 premier	2 deux	3 trois	4 quatre	5 cinq	6 six
7 sept	8 huit	9 neuf	10 dix	11 onze	12 douze	13 treize
14 quatorze	15 quinze	16 seize	17 dix-sept	18 dix-huit	19 dix-neuf	20 vingt
21 vingt et un	22 vingt-deux	23 vingt-trois	24 vingt-quatre	25 vingt-cinq	26 vingt-six	27 vingt-sept
28 vingt-huit	29 vingt-neuf	30 trente	31 trente et un			

LES GRANDES DATES, 2019

le 1er janvier	le premier de l'an
le 14 février	la Saint Valentin
le 5 mars	Mardi Gras
le 21 avril	Pâques
le 1er mai	la fête du Travail
le 8 mai	la fête de la Victoire de la deuxième guerre mondiale (1945)
le 30 mai	l'Ascension
le 9 juin	la Pentecôte
le 14 juillet	la fête nationale
le 1er novembre	la Toussaint
le 11 novembre	l'Armistice de la première guerre mondiale (1918)
le 25 décembre	Noël

février
lu	ma	me	je	ve	sa	di
				1	2	3
4	5	6	7	8	9	10
11	12	13	14	15	16	17
18	19	20	21	22	23	24
25	26	27	28			

mars
lu	ma	me	je	ve	sa	di
				1	2	3
4	5	6	7	8	9	10
11	12	13	14	15	16	17
18	19	20	21	22	23	24
25	26	27	28	29	30	31

avril
lu	ma	me	je	ve	sa	di
1	2	3	4	5	6	7
8	9	10	11	12	13	14
15	16	17	18	19	20	21
22	23	24	25	26	27	28
29	30					

mai
lu	ma	me	je	ve	sa	di
		1	2	3	4	5
6	7	8	9	10	11	12
13	14	15	16	17	18	19
20	21	22	23	24	25	26
27	28	29	30	31		

juin
lu	ma	me	je	ve	sa	di
					1	2
3	4	5	6	7	8	9
10	11	12	13	14	15	16
17	18	19	20	21	22	23
24	25	26	27	28	29	30

juillet
lu	ma	me	je	ve	sa	di
1	2	3	4	5	6	7
8	9	10	11	12	13	14
15	16	17	18	19	20	21
22	23	24	25	26	27	28
29	30	31				

août
lu	ma	me	je	ve	sa	di
			1	2	3	4
5	6	7	8	9	10	11
12	13	14	15	16	17	18
19	20	21	22	23	24	25
26	27	28	29	30	31	

septembre
lu	ma	me	je	ve	sa	di
						1
2	3	4	5	6	7	8
9	10	11	12	13	14	15
16	17	18	19	20	21	22
23	24	25	26	27	28	29
30						

octobre
lu	ma	me	je	ve	sa	di
1	2	3	4	5	6	
7	8	9	10	11	12	13
14	15	16	17	18	19	20
21	22	23	24	25	26	27
28	29	30	31			

novembre
lu	ma	me	je	ve	sa	di
			1	2	3	
4	5	6	7	8	9	10
11	12	13	14	15	16	17
18	19	20	21	22	23	24
25	26	27	28	29	30	

décembre
lu	ma	me	je	ve	sa	di
						1
2	3	4	5	6	7	8
9	10	11	12	13	14	15
16	17	18	19	20	21	22
23	24	25	26	27	28	29
30	31					

Activité 16

💬 Les numéros de 1 à 31

Working with a **partenaire** (*partner*), count from 1 to 31, forwards and backwards, and again skipping odd, then even numbers.

Activité 17

  Les dates

Listen and mark the dates read by your teacher.

Activité 18

Mon anniversaire

> Bonjour, Bruno! C'est quand ton anniversaire?

> Mon anniversaire est le 24 mars.

 Mon progrès communicatif

I can say the date, the day of the week, the month of the year, and my birthday.

💬 Étape 1 : Parlez

Practice with a ***partenaire*** saying your own birthday in French.

Modèle

Élève A: Mon anniversaire est le 19 septembre.

Élève B: Mon anniversaire est le 28 avril.

Étape 2: Écoutez

C'est quel jour mon anniversaire? (*On what day is my birthday?*) You need to check on which day of the week birthdays of several students fall. Listen to each date, locate it on the 2019 calendar from France and then write the day of the week on which the birthday falls.

1. _____   4. _____

2. _____   5. _____

3. _____   6. _____

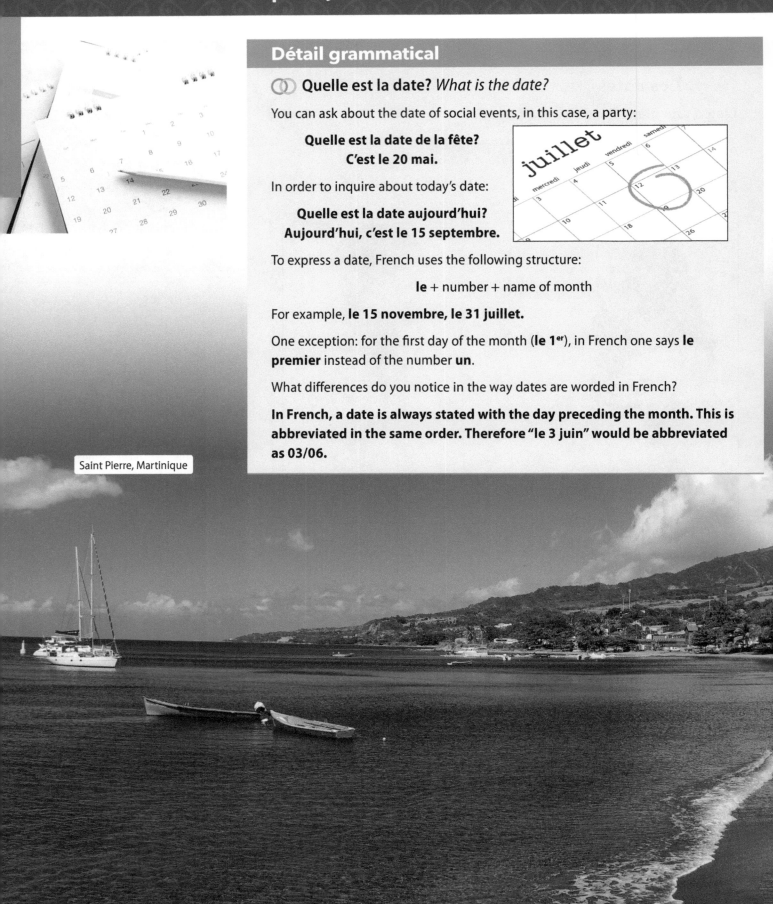

Détail grammatical

◑ Quelle est la date? *What is the date?*

You can ask about the date of social events, in this case, a party:

Quelle est la date de la fête?
C'est le 20 mai.

In order to inquire about today's date:

Quelle est la date aujourd'hui?
Aujourd'hui, c'est le 15 septembre.

To express a date, French uses the following structure:

le + number + name of month

For example, **le 15 novembre, le 31 juillet.**

One exception: for the first day of the month (**le 1er**), in French one says **le premier** instead of the number **un**.

What differences do you notice in the way dates are worded in French?

In French, a date is always stated with the day preceding the month. This is abbreviated in the same order. Therefore "le 3 juin" would be abbreviated as 03/06.

Saint Pierre, Martinique

Prononciation

▶️ 🧭 Final Consonants

A pronunciation concept that sets French apart from many other languages like English and Spanish, is the fact that much of the time, the final letter of a word is silent, meaning that it is not pronounced.

If a word ends in a consonant, this final letter will generally not be pronounced. Here are some examples of this (note that the silent consonant is crossed out):

deux	the x is silent
ans	the s is silent
comment	the t is silent

There are a few exceptions to this rule, when the final consonant is pronounced, such as:

mars

avril

août

Activité 19

Les numéros de téléphone

📖 **Étape 1: Lisez**

Read the *Zoom culture* concerning French phone numbers and complete the grid below with the two digit phone prefix that would be affiliated with the phone number of the person being described.

description de la personne	image de la région	indicatif téléphonique (01, 02...)
Pierre Clémont lives in the town of Cannes with a magnificent view of the Mediterranean Sea and organizes the Cannes Film Festival.		
Mélanie Dufour conducts tours of the Normandy beaches where American, Canadian and British forces landed to defeat the Axis forces during World War II.		
Yannick Diop is an archaeologist who conducts research on man's early history near the Lascaux caves.		
Sylvie Caudet is a mechanical engineer who works at the Eiffel Tower, ensuring the mechanical soundness of this symbol of Paris that opened in 1889.		
Claude Leblanc works at Champagne producer Moët et Chandon as a supervisor in the nearly 28 km of underground caves that store millions of bottles.		

Zoom culture

Pratique culturelle: Téléphoner en France

  Connexions

Think about telephone numbers that you know.

1. How are they created?

2. Do any parts of the telephone number have a special significance or meaning?

Since 1996, phone numbers in France contain ten digits grouped in pairs, so a typical French phone number would look like - 03 14 31 22 29. This number would be read as ***zéro trois, quatorze, trente et un, vingt-deux, vingt-neuf***. The first two digits of the phone number are the equivalent of an area code. Here is a list of those two digit codes along with a map that explains their location:

- **01** Île-de-France - including Paris, the capital of France featuring iconic locations such as the Louvre museum, the Eiffel Tower and the Arc of Triumph.

- **02** Northwest France - including the region of Normandy, where Allied forces landed on the beaches on June 6, 1944, turning the tide of WWII in favor of the Allies.

- **03** Northeast France - including the Champagne region, famous for its bubbly wine.

- **04** Southeast France - including the fabled French Riviera (***La Côte d'Azur***) with its picturesque Mediterranean beaches.

- **05** Southwest France - including the world famous Lascaux caves, whose walls are adorned with paintings that date back nearly 20,000 years.

- **06 and 07** - Mobile phone services.

  Réflexion

Compare some of these facts about phone numbers and phone use to how you might use phones where you live.

  Étape 2: Écoutez et écrivez

Listen to the following French phone numbers. Then fill in the ten digit number in the spaces provided.

Modèle

You hear - "***zéro trois, vingt, onze, vingt-deux, quatorze***". You would write " <u>03</u> <u>20</u> <u>11</u> <u>22</u> <u>14</u>"

1. ____   ____   ____   ____   ____

2. ____   ____   ____   ____   ____

3. ____   ____   ____   ____   ____

4. ____   ____   ____   ____   ____

5. ____   ____   ____   ____   ____

Mon progrès communicatif

I can recognize and use numbers to express phone numbers.

Aïssa Maïga

Qui es-tu?

📖 🎤 Étape 1: Lisez et préparez

Form groups of six students. Each person in the group should assume the identity of one of the famous people depicted in the images on this page and memorize his or her birthday. Practice saying your identity to yourself with: *"Je m'appelle _____. Mon anniversaire est le _____."*

🎧 Étape 2: Écoutez et parlez

Listen as your teacher says the birth dates of the famous people. When you hear your famous person's birth date, raise your hand, and say your identity. The first person to correctly say his or her identity on the right date gets a point for his or her team.

Modèle

Professeur: Ton anniversaire est le _____.

Élève: C'est moi. Je m'appelle _____.

Léopold Senghor
le 9 octobre

Coco Chanel
le 19 août

Victor Hugo
le 26 février

Yannick Noah
le 18 mai

Louis XIV
le 5 septembre

Edith Piaf
le 10 octobre

Activité 21

Les Fêtes de Bayonne

 ✦ **Étape 1: Lisez**

Look at the poster and the picture from France. They depict scenes in the streets of a famous city during the *Fêtes de Bayonne*. Describe what you see and what you think happens at this event.

Archives Ville de Bayonne, auteur: Arnaud Saez.

Tenue traditionnelle des Fêtes de Bayonne.

Find the following:

1. the dates of the *Fêtes de Bayonne*

2. the city where the festival takes place

3. the word in French for:
   party/celebration
   outfit(s)

Watch this video in Explorer to practice using these Interpretive Print strategies.

Stratégies

 Interpretive Print

Strategies help you use what you know to help communicate and understand even when you are just starting to learn French. In this video, you will learn five reading strategies that will help you understand ads for schools, camps and other programs.

1. Make predictions about what you will read

2. Use pictures and graphics to get the main idea

3. Use words that you have learned to get some detail

4. Use cognates but be careful

5. Use logic and make educated guesses

 Étape 2: Regardez et identifiez

You are going to watch a video that illustrates different events that happen during the **Fêtes de Bayonne**. As you watch, identify the activities that are shown in the video by putting a ✓. Most of the words listed below are **cognates** - words that look like and mean something similar to a word you already know.

____ danser

____ chanter

____ le cinéma

____ la musique

____ l'exercice

____ le football

____ les concerts

Étape 3: Parlez

juillet 2019

lundi	mardi	mercredi	jeudi	vendredi	samedi	dimanche
1	2	3	4	5	6	7
8	9	10	11	12	13	14
15	16	17	18	19	20	21
22	23	24	25	26	27	28
29	30	31				

The dates for the **Fêtes de Bayonne** 2019 are July 24–28. Use the calendar provided to identify on which day of the week each date falls, then, with a **partenaire**, take turns reading these dates in French.

Modèle

mercredi, vingt-quatre juillet

Zoom culture

Produit et pratique culturels: Un grand festival

   Connexions

1. What symbols are important to the identity of your community/state/country? (Think of animals, flowers, or other mascots.)

2. Are there any symbols that are linked to a connection with another country?

The **Fêtes de Bayonne** is the largest yearly festival in France. Over one million people gather in Bayonne for this celebration. This four-day and five-night festival first started in 1932 to recreate a celebration similar to the running of the bulls in Pamplona, Spain. The original colors worn for the festival were white and blue (traditional colors of the city of Bayonne). The colors were changed to white and red in later years to align with the Pamplona festival colors.

Le **béret**, a very traditional soft and round hat, is widely recognized as a symbol of French fashion and culture.

Painting of a group of musicians during the **Fêtes de Bayonne** wearing the traditional white and red clothing and the red **béret** (painted by impressionist artist Patrick Larcebal).

Réflexion

Would you like to attend the **Fêtes de Bayonne**? Why or why not?

Mon progrès communicatif

I can recognize some words related to activities in a promotional video.

✏️ 🗣️ Étape 4: Écrivez et comparez

Which festivals, holidays, or events are important in your culture? Create a list of the four most important events and dates and try to express the name in French. Use a dictionary or ask **"Comment dit-on _____?"** to get your teacher's help. Then compare your list with those of your classmates to see which events are repeated.

Modèle

1. Noël est le 25 décembre.

Bayonne, France

✏️ ✳️ Étape 5: Écrivez

Create a simple song or poem based on a date that is important in your culture. For example, the model below is about the United States' Independence Day, the Fourth of July. If you prefer, use your birthday as inspiration for the poem.

Modèle

Le premier avril
Le deux mai
Le trois juin
Le quatre juillet
Indépendance!

Réflexion interculturelle

⊙⊙ ✳️ How do people celebrate local and national holidays in your community? What are some symbols associated with the holidays? Based on what you learned about Francophone local and national holidays, what are some similarities and differences?

Provide the information requested or answer the questions in the discussion forum in Explorer.

Mon progrès interculturel

I can identify how Francophone cultures and my culture celebrate local and national holidays or festivals.

Activité 22

Activités pour l'été

Since you are interested in what teens do on summer vacation in Francophone countries, you searched online and found this ad. Be sure to use the vocabulary and strategies you have learned to understand the purpose of the ad.

New Caledonia

📖 ✪ Étape 1: Identifiez

Identify the dates, ages, and prices listed. Using what you know, make a prediction as to the purpose of the ad.

📝 ✪ Étape 2: Écrivez

Create a list of cognates in this ad and identify what you think these words might mean in English. Be sure to use the pictures to help you!

📖 ✪ Étape 3: Évaluez

What do you think this ad is designed to promote? Now that you have identified the meaning of much of the information in this ad, update the prediction you made in *Étape 1* to reflect all the information and pictures that were provided.

✪ **Mon progrès communicatif**

I can identify the purpose of an advertisement.

Activité 23

📖 **C'est quelle année?**

Look at the image below. Can you find the French expression for "Happy New Year"?

bonne année
bonne
baxtalo nevo bersh
Chúc Mừng Năm Mới
سال نو
sun nien fai lok
Shana tova
مبارک
feliz año nuevo
Xin nian yu kuai
新年快乐
bonu annu nou

Activité 24

🎧 ✹ **Les numéros de 2000 à 2020**

Listen to the numbers 2000-2020. Use your finger to follow along in the image above. What expression do you hear for "two thousand?"

2000	2001	2002	2003	2004
2005	2006	2007	2008	2009
2010	2011	2012	2013	2014
	2015	2016	2017	
	2018	2019	2020	

Activité 25

📖 🎧 ✹ **Victoires de la musique française**

Listen to the year that some famous songs won the *Victoires de la musique française* award (French equivalent to the Grammys, awarded by the French Ministry of Culture). When you hear the year, consult the table and write the name of the artist who recorded the song that year.

Modèle

"Le dîner" (*"The dinner"*) **a gagné** (*won*) Les Victoires de la musique en **deux mille sept**.

Artiste: Bénabar.

Bénabar, chanteur français.

année	chanson	artiste
2000	Tomber la chemise	Zebda
2001	L'envie d'aimer	Daniel Lévi
2002	Sous le vent	Garou et Céline Dion
2003	Manhattan-Kaboul	Renaud et Axelle Red
2004	Respire	Mickey 3-D
2005	Si seulement je pouvais lui manquer	Calogero
2006	Caravane	Raphael
2007	Le dîner	Bénabar
2008	Double je	Christophe Willem
2009	Comme un manouche sans guitare	Thomas Dutronc
2010	Comme des enfants	Coeur de Pirate
2011	Je veux	Zaz
2012	Jeanne	Laurent Voulzy
2013	Allez allez allez	Camille
2014	20 ans	Johnny Hallyday
2015	Un jour au mauvais endroit	Calogero

Céline Dion, chanteuse québécoise

Laurent Voulzy, chanteur et compositeur français

Activité 26

Les années importantes de ma vie

 ⊕ **Étape 1: Écrivez**

When did the important events in your life happen? Fill out the **je/moi** column of the chart with the relevant years; write the numerals.

Camille, chanteuse française

💬 🧭 Étape 2: Demandez et répondez

Ask your **partenaire** when his or her important events happened by asking **En quelle année…?** (*In what year…?*) and pointing to an event from the list. Your **partenaire** should answer with a year in French, e.g., **2005** (**deux mille cinq**). Jot down the year (use numerals) in the space provided. If the year matches what you wrote, say "**Moi aussi**" ("*Me too*"). Reverse roles and answer the questions from your **partenaire**.

les années importantes de ma vie	je/moi	mon/ma partenaire
the year you were born		
the year you started school		
the year you expect to graduate from high school		
the year you visited or hope to visit a French-speaking country		
the year you…		

Parc national des volcans, Rwanda

Zoom culture

Pratique culturelle: Les années

  Connexions

1. How do you say these dates in English: 1900, 1905, 1917, 2000, 2005, 2011, 2016?

2. Is there more than one acceptable way to say some years? Give examples. Answer in the discussion forum in Explorer.

There are two ways of expressing years before 2000 in French. For example, the year 1960 could be expressed in two different ways. The more frequently used method is ***mille neuf cent soixante***. However, you may see or hear that date as ***dix-neuf cent soixante***. The years after 2000, such as 2017, are expressed like this: ***deux mille dix-sept***.

  Réflexion

How do the ways dates are expressed in French compare to how dates are expressed in English?

Vocabulaire

Comment dit-on? 1: I can ask and answer questions to meet and greet a young person.

Premières conversations	Greetings and responses
bonjour	*hello*
salut	*hi*
Comment ça va?	*How are you? (informal)*
Comment allez-vous?	*How are you? (formal)*
Ça va bien. Et toi?	*I'm fine. And you?*
Ça va très bien, merci.	*I'm very well, thanks.*
Comment t'appelles-tu?	*What's your name?*
Je m'appelle…	*My name is…*
D'où viens-tu?	*Where are you from?*
Je viens de…	*I'm from…*
ciao	*ciao*
au revoir	*good-bye*

Comment dit-on? 2: I can follow classroom commands.

Les expressions dans la salle de classe	*Classroom expressions*
asseyez-vous	*sit down*
écoutez	*listen*
fermez vos livres	*close your books*
il vous faut…	*you need…*
levez la main	*raise your hand*
levez-vous	*stand up*
ouvrez vos livres	*open your books*
parlez avec votre voisin	*talk to your neighbor*
parlez en français	*speak in French*
regardez-moi	*look at me*
répétez	*repeat*
retournez à vos places	*go back to your seats*
s'il vous plaît	*please*

Comment dit-on? 3: I can say the date, the day of the week, the month of the year, and my birthday.

Les numéros de 1 à 31 — Numbers 1 through 31

1 un	11 onze	21 vingt et un	
2 deux	12 douze	22 vingt-deux	
3 trois	13 treize	23 vingt-trois	
4 quatre	14 quatorze	24 vingt-quatre	
5 cinq	15 quinze	25 vingt-cinq	
6 six	16 seize	26 vingt-six	
7 sept	17 dix-sept	27 vingt-sept	
8 huit	18 dix-huit	28 vingt-huit	
9 neuf	19 dix-neuf	29 vingt-neuf	
10 dix	20 vingt	30 trente	
		31 trente et un	

Les mois de l'année — Months of the year

janvier	*January*
février	*February*
mars	*March*
avril	*April*
mai	*May*
juin	*June*
juillet	*July*
août	*August*
septembre	*September*
octobre	*October*
novembre	*November*
décembre	*December*

Les jours de la semaine — Days of the week

lundi	*Monday*
mardi	*Tuesday*
mercredi	*Wednesday*
jeudi	*Thursday*
vendredi	*Friday*
samedi	*Saturday*
dimanche	*Sunday*

Les dates — Dates

C'est quand ton anniversaire?	*When is your birthday?*
Mon anniversaire est le…	*My birthday is the…*
Quelle est la date?	*What is the date?*
C'est le + numéro + mois	*It's month + number*
le premier	*the first (day of month)*

J'y arrive

Questions essentielles

- How do I begin and maintain a simple conversation when meeting a French speaker?

- What strategies will help me communicate in French as I begin to learn the language?

Les colonies de vacances

Young people all over the world attend summer camps in order to learn or improve a new skill. Imagine you decide to go a ***colonie de vacances*** *(summer camp)* in France to immerse yourself in French. You will read an ad on a website about some of the camps offered in France. When you arrive, you will meet young people speaking French so you will have the opportunity to introduce yourself and ask and answer a few questions to get to know someone.

Before you begin, refer to the ***J'y arrive*** rubric in Explorer to familiarize yourself with the evaluation criteria.

Interpretive Assessment

   Étape 1: Identifiez

Cognates are words that look and have a similar meaning in two languages. Look at the ad for summer camp and find six cognates between French and English.

Étape 2: Lisez

Look at the page from a website describing summer camp opportunities in France. Read the information and select the camp that is best suited for you. Use cognates to support your answers.

LES SÉJOURS

Danse hip-hop

10 à 15 ans

À partir de
840€

- Découvrir la danse hip-hop et ses différents styles
- Apprendre à créer sa propre chorégraphie
- Préparer un spectacle de fin de séjour!

Programming informatique

13 à 17 ans

À partir de
759€

- Utiliser différents langages de programmation
- Découvrir l'environnement mobile
- Développer votre propre appli iphone!

Future vétérinaire

12 à 17 ans

À partir de
685€

- Observer et apprendre à prendre soin d'animaux de ferme
- Préparer et distribuer la nourriture
- Assister à certains soins médicaux

Telligo (2017), "Les séjours", Recreated from http://www.telligo.fr.

Étape 3: Écoutez

You have selected your ***colonie de vacances*** and travel to France for this camp. You attend the introductory meeting on the first day to meet other young people at the camp. Everyone is introducing themselves, so jot down the information you hear on the chart provided in Explorer.

	personne 1	**personne 2**	**personne 3**
nom			
âge			
origine			
anniversaire			

Interpersonal Assessment

Une conversation

After the introductory meeting, the person sitting next to you begins a conversation. Ask and answer questions appropriately, following the instructions in Explorer.

UNITÉ 1
L'identité

Objectifs de l'unité

Interact to express your identity, ask for and give personal information, and express preferences about activities.

Interpret images, video, and audio, and print texts in French to gain insights into identity.

Present basic information about yourself.

Investigate, explain and reflect on the role of language in shaping identity in France, Quebec, and in your community.

✤ Questions essentielles

Who am I? How does what I do define who I am?

How do I exchange information about my identity and that of others?

What are cultural similarities and differences between myself and others in a Francophone community?

There are many sides to our identity. We may be students, athletes, artists and volunteers. In this unit, you will learn to talk with French speakers about who you are and start to develop another aspect of your identity: bilingual communicator connecting across cultures.

Nom: Marianne

Langues parlées: français, anglais, espagnol, italien

Origine: Montréal, Québec, Canada

La province de Québec partage une frontière avec quatre états américains: le Maine, le New Hampshire, le New York et le Vermont.

«Je me souviens» signifie "*I remember*" en anglais. Les Québécois considèrent leur relation culturelle et linguistique avec la France très importante.

Rencontre interculturelle

Across the course of the six units of this book, you will meet each of our bloggers. In this first unit, you will get to know Marianne and François. Each will share information about themselves and their backgrounds through video blogs. You will encounter them repeatedly throughout the textbook.

Le Québec

La France commence à explorer l'Atlantique en 1534. Les colonies s'appellent la Nouvelle-France. Aujourd'hui, une grande partie de l'ancienne Nouvelle-France s'appelle le Québec.

Samuel de Champlain fonde la ville de Québec en 1608. La ville de Québec est la plus ancienne ville francophone en Amérique du Nord.

Samuel de Champlain, explorateur

Nombre de personnes qui parlent français

● Montréal, Québec, Canada	● Canada	● Paris, France	● France
3.824.221	10.523.000	12.161.542	65.342.000

Montréal, une grande ville francophone

La France

La France est un pays européen entouré à l'ouest par l'océan Atlantique et au sud par la mer Méditerranée. Elle partage ses frontières avec l'Espagne, Monaco, l'Italie, la Suisse, le Luxembourg, l'Allemagne, l'Andorre et la Belgique.

La France a aussi des territoires dans l'océan Indien (la Réunion et Mayotte), dans les Caraïbes (la Guadeloupe et la Martinique) et en Amérique du Sud (la Guyane).

La France est une destination touristique importante.

FRANCE

Nom: François

Langues parlées: français, anglais, espagnol

Origine: Amiens, France

La France - Première destination touristique

84,2 millions
la France

66,7 millions
les États-Unis

65 millions
l'Espagne

Personnages français avec un impact global et historique

L'équipe nationale de foot de France gagne la Coupe du monde en 2018.

Napoléon Bonaparte, général et empereur de France

Jacques Cousteau, explorateur marin

Jeanne d'Arc, héroïne de l'histoire

Coco Chanel, créatrice de mode

Both Marianne and François speak French, but you'll notice that their French sounds different because they come from different areas of the Francophone world. The French that they speak is the same language, but you will notice a different accent, just as you would when listening to people speaking English who come from different places such as Alabama, New York or London.

Le Québec

Je m'appelle Marianne.

Je suis du Québec.

Je suis athlète.

J'aime le soccer

La France

Je m'appelle François.

Je suis un élève.

J'ai 15 ans.

J'étudie l'anglais et l'espagnol.

J'habite à Amiens au nord de Paris.

Marianne est de Montréal, au Canada.

François est un élève au collège (*middle school*) à Amiens, en France.

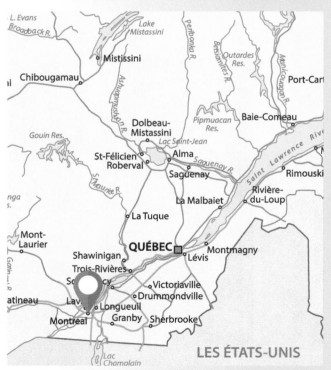

Le Québec est près des états américains du Maine, du New Hampshire, du Vermont et du New York.

Le système scolaire en France

6–10 ans	11–15 ans	16–18 ans
l'école primaire	le collège (l'école secondaire)	le lycée (l'école secondaire)

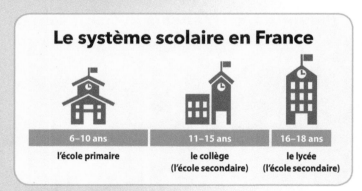

Amiens est une ville au nord de la France, près de Paris.

Bonjour, Marianne et François!

Record your responses to the following in the discussion forum in Explorer.

📖 🧭 Étape 1: Préparez

Look at the pictures of Marianne and François and what is in their speech bubbles. What kind of information do you think they have included in their video blogs? What do you think the phrases in the speech bubbles mean?

▶️ 🧭 Étape 2: Écoutez

Listen to the video blogs and raise your hand when you think you hear Marianne and François say the words from the picture captions.

▶️ 🧭 Étape 3: Résumez

Listen and watch again. Based on what you see and hear, write two sentences about what you think Marianne and François are telling us in their video blogs.

◎ 🧭 Étape 4: Comparez

How are Marianne and François similar to you? How are they different? Share your observations in class and in your *EntreCultures 1* Explorer course.

◎ 🧭 What did you notice in the video about what Marianne and François like and don't like? She likes playing soccer and hanging out with friends and family. He says he likes to skateboard and read comics, but doesn't like doing homework. Are these likes and dislikes similar or different from yours? Do you think playing sports in Quebec is the same as in your school? Do you think homework in France poses the same or different challenges than homework in your school? In preparation for answering the questions in the discussion forum in Explorer, complete the *diagramme de Venn* first.

Le Carnaval d'hiver de Québec

La plus grande cathédrale en France est à Amiens!

🧭 **Mon progrès interculturel**

I can identify some similarities and differences between Francophone young people and myself.

📊 📊 📊

Communiquons

Comment dit-on? 1

✦ **Qui suis-je?**

Je suis **bilingue.**
J'aime parler français
et anglais.

Je suis **élève.**
J'aime étudier.

Je suis **musicien.**
J'aime jouer de la musique.

Je suis **athlète** et
je suis **sportif.**
J'aime jouer au hockey.

Je suis
sérieux.
J'aime travailler
et écouter.

Je suis **sérieuse.**
J'aime travailler et
écouter aussi.

Je suis **chanteuse.**
J'aime chanter et écouter
de la musique.

Je suis
américain.
J'aime habiter
aux États-Unis.

Je suis
américaine.
J'aime voyager en
Californie.

Je suis **artiste.**
J'aime dessiner et peindre.

Activité 2

🎧 ✦ **Qui suis-je?**

Look at the photographs under *Comment dit-on? 1*. Then listen
to the six speakers and write down the letter of the picture that
corresponds to the speaker's identity.

1. _____ 2. _____ 3. _____ 4. _____ 5. _____ 6. _____ 7. _____ 8. _____

Activité 3

  Es-tu bilingue?

Your teacher will ask you a series of questions about your identity. Listen carefully and follow the model to respond.

Modèle

Professeur: Es-tu bilingue?

Élève: Oui, je suis bilingue./Non, je ne suis pas bilingue.

Zoom culture

Perspective culturelle: Justin Trudeau, un Canadien à plusieurs identités

  Connexions

How do politicians in your community share their identities?

Justin Trudeau is the 23rd Prime Minister of Canada. However, before becoming a politician, he was a math and French teacher. He is bilingual, having grown up in a family that brought together the English and French influences throughout Canada. In his politics, he is a strong advocate of education and programs for young people, as well as the environment. The son of a former Prime Minister, Trudeau now has three children of his own.

  Réflexion

Research the life and career of Justin Trudeau. How does he self-identify, both personally and professionally? Which perspectives does a bilingual politician bring to your community?

Stratégies

Interpretive Listening

When listening to French, relax! You won't understand everything. Your goal for now is to understand a few familiar words and phrases as you listen. With practice, you will understand more.

Watch the listening strategies video in Explorer for more tips to help you understand spoken French.

Remember these tips:

1. Pay attention. Don't panic.

2. Note the words you understand.

3. Observe visual cues.

On peut aussi dire

Qui suis-je?

acteur/actrice

bénévole

blogueur/blogueuse

créateur/créatrice de mode

cycliste

danseur/danseuse

explorateur/exploratrice

inventeur/inventrice

photographe

poète

scientifique

Mon progrès communicatif

I can ask and answer simple questions about identity.

Activité 4

Mon identité et ton identité

  Étape 1: Écrivez

Look at the list of identities in the chart and write **oui** or **non** in the first column (under **moi**) to indicate if they correspond or do not correspond to your identity.

les identités	moi	élève 1	élève 2	élève 3
musicien/ musicienne*				
athlète				
élève				
chanteur/ chanteuse				
artiste				
bilingue				
américain/ américaine				
sérieux/ sérieuse				

*If there are two versions of the word listed, use the first one (**musicien**) for a male and the second one (**musicienne**) for a female.

Étape 2: Demandez

Ask questions to three of your classmates, following this pattern, and record their answers in the chart in **Étape 1**.

Modèle

Élève A: Es-tu musicien(ne)?

Élève B: Non, je ne suis pas musicien(ne).

Élève A: Es-tu athlète?

Élève B: Oui, je suis athlète.

Activité 5

Des identités supplémentaires

 Étape 1: Parlez

How many of the other identities listed in *On peut aussi dire* can you understand without using a dictionary?

A

B

C

D

E

F

Étape 2: Identifiez

Write the identity represented in each photograph.

A. _____cycliste_____

B. _____

C. _____

D. _____

E. _____

F. _____

Étape 3: Décrivez

Which of these additional words would you use to describe yourself? Write sentences with *Je suis* _____.

On peut aussi dire

Qui suis-je?

actif/active

ambitieux/ambitieuse

canadien/canadienne

courageux/courageuse

français/française

généreux/généreuse

québécois/québécoise

végétarien/végétarienne

Détail grammatical

Les noms masculins/féminins

If there are two forms listed, the first one refers to a male (*masculin [m.]*), and the second one to a female (*féminin [f.]*). Note that some of the masculine forms end in *-eux* or *-eur* and the feminine forms may end in *-euse* or *-rice*. Also, some masculine forms may end in *-if* and the feminine form may end in *-ive*.

Mon progrès communicatif

I can understand words relating to identity to describe myself and others.

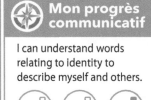

Gérard Depardieu, acteur français

Tableau de Claude Monet, artiste impressionniste

Jodie Foster, actrice américaine qui parle français

Activité 6

Les identités des personnes célèbres

One's profession is often an important part of one's identity.

💬 Étape 1: Demandez

Can you match these famous French speakers with their identity? Ask your **partenaire** some questions, connecting the person's name and identity with **est**, as in the model. Look up the people you don't know or consult a classmate to fill in the gaps in your knowledge.

Modèle

Élève A: Qui est Gérard Depardieu?

Élève B: Gérard Depardieu est acteur.

Les gens célèbres	Les professions
1. Coco Chanel	acteur/actrice
2. Claude Monet	
3. Céline Dion	artiste
4. Bradley Cooper	
5. Christian Dior	chanteur/chanteuse
6. Avril Lavigne	créateur/créatrice de mode
7. Emmanuel Macron	
8. Jodie Foster	président
9. Stromae	

BONJOUR
JE M'APELLE

✎ ✦ Étape 2: Associez

Match each image of a well-known French speaker or product to the name and a descriptor.

  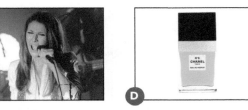

Céline Dion	général
Napoléon	chanteur/chanteuse
Zinedine Zidane	canadien/canadienne
Stromae	québécois/québécoise
Coco Chanel	français/française
Louis Pasteur	scientifique
Marion Cotillard	actrice
Avril Lavigne	créatrice de mode
	athlète

A. _____ _____   B. _____ _____

C. _____ _____   D. _____ _____

E. _____ _____   F. _____ _____

G. _____ _____   H. _____ _____

Réflexion interculturelle

🌐 ✦ Which personalities interest you most? With whom were you familiar? About whom would you like to know more and why? Investigate at least one person on the list about whom you did not know anything. Provide the information requested or answer the questions in the discussion forum in Explorer.

✦ Mon progrès interculturel

I can identify some famous French speakers, their professions, and their contributions.

📶 📶 📶

Découvrons 1

Expressing Who I Am

> *Je parle français et espagnol. Et toi, tu **es** bilingue?*

> *Oui, moi aussi. Je **suis** bilingue. Je parle français et italien.*

Découvertes

▶ ✦ Read the dialogue above and notice the words in bold used to introduce identities (***es***, ***suis***). What do you observe about the different forms? Can you figure out when to use ***es*** and ***suis***? Discuss with classmates and teacher, view the ***Découvrons 1*** resources for this unit in your Explorer course, and check the ***Synthèse de grammaire*** at the end of this unit.

Activité 7

Vingt questions: Mon identité

✏️ Étape 1: Écrivez

Look at these words. Select and write five words that describe your identity. Don't let anyone else see your words!

Noms	**Adjectifs**
acteur/actrice	actif/active
artiste	ambitieux/ambitieuse
chanteur/chanteuse	courageux/courageuse
créateur/créatrice de mode	sérieux/sérieuse
cycliste	sportif/sportive
élève	timide
photographe	

💬 Étape 2: Demandez et répondez

Working with a **partenaire**, ask questions like the ones in the model until your **partenaire** answers affirmatively based on his or her list from **Étape 1**. Then switch roles. **Note**: Read the **Détail grammatical** concerning the verb **être** to help you use complete sentences in your answer.

Modèle

Tu es sportif/sportive?

Est-ce que tu es chanteur/chanteuse?

Détail grammatical

Le verbe être

The verb **être** is the most commonly used verb in French and is one way to express identity.

je suis	*I am*
tu es	*you (familiar/ informal); are*
elle est	*she is*
il est	*he is*

To make the above forms negative, surround the verb form with the words *ne... pas*:

je **ne** suis **pas**
tu **n'**es **pas**
il/elle **n'**est **pas**

Mon progrès communicatif

I can ask and answer simple questions about identity.

Prononciation

Le son /r/

The French **r** is pronounced in the throat, as opposed to the English **r**, which is pronounced in the front of the mouth. You can practice making this sound by gargling with water. Notice that you can gargle while making a sound with your voice and also by simply blowing air through your throat. This is true with the French **r** as well, depending on the word. Your mouth must be open to pronounce the French **r**. The exact shape of your mouth depends upon which sounds are before or after the **r** in the particular word. Look at the following words and listen to François pronounce them. Also notice the shape of his mouth while he says them.

ré**r**étez	géné**r**eux
f**r**ançais	bonjou**r**
c**r**oissant	c**r**éateu**r**
cou**r**ageuse	

Now practice saying these words yourself, trying to imitate how François, the native speaker, pronounces them. Bravo!

Mon progrès communicatif

I can write some simple sentences about identity.

Activité 8

C'est qui?

Now that you know the identities of some famous French-speakers, your classmates, and perhaps your teacher, see how many simple sentences you can write about them.

Modèles

Sophie est artiste.

Paul est actif.

Madame Leblanc n'est pas photographe.

J'avance 1

Les identités

✏️ 🧭 Étape 1: Écrivez

Think of four people you know well and who are different from each other (different backgrounds, ages, interests…). Can you think of words and/or simple sentences you have learned to talk about their identities? List as many as possible for each person.

A member of your family	A classmate	Another classmate	An adult in your community

💬 🧭 Étape 2: Demandez et répondez

Pair up with a student in your class whom you have not yet met. Ask and answer questions to find out as much as you can about him/her. Add the information you learn about your *partenaire* to the chart in *Étape 1.* Record your entire conversation in Explorer and remember that all of the materials for *J'avance 1* can be found in Explorer.

🧭 **Mon progrès communicatif**

I can ask and answer simple questions about identity.

📶 📶 📶

Le Rocher de Monaco à gauche et le quartier Fontvieille à droite.

Comment dit-on? 2

✦ Mes activités préférées

J'aime

1. écouter de la musique

2. danser

3. manger

4. lire

5. jouer

6. surfer sur internet

7. regarder une série/un film

8. passer du temps avec des amis

9. aller au café/cinéma

10. dessiner

11. étudier

12. jouer de la musique

Activité 9

  Quelle identité?

Listen to the speakers share their favorite activity and select the correct identity.

1. a. inventeur b. musicienne
2. a. photographe b. bénévole
3. a. blogueur b. végétarien
4. a. cycliste b. danseuse
5. a. poète b. élève
6. a. athlète b. musicien
7. a. artiste b. explorateur

Activité 10

  Logique ou illogique

Which of these sentences are logical? Rewrite the illogical sentences so they make sense.

Modèle

Je suis athlète; j'aime jouer du piano.

illogique: Je suis athlète; j'aime jouer au football.

1. Je suis artiste; j'aime dessiner.
2. J'aime surfer sur internet; je suis musicien.
3. Je suis une élève; j'aime étudier le français.
4. J'aime danser; je suis photographe.
5. J'aime manger des hamburgers; je suis végétarien.

On peut aussi dire

chanter	*to sing*
discuter	*to discuss*
dormir	*to sleep*
écrire	*to write*
habiter	*to live*
jouer aux jeux vidéo	*to play video games*
peindre	*to paint*
travailler	*to work*
voyager	*to travel*

Mon progrès communicatif

I can understand some words and phrases relating to activity preferences.

Zoom culture

Pratique culturelle: Le handball

  Connexions

Which sports are most popular where you live? Are these sports played around the world, or just in your geographic area? Why do you think that is?

Le handball is one of the most popular sports in France (with soccer, rugby, tennis and cycling). This sport, which originated in Germany, is played in teams of seven, either indoor or outdoors, though for competitions, it is generally played inside. Equally popular for girls and boys, *le handball*, is played using only the players' hands, as its name implies. France's national women's and men's handball teams both earned silver medals in the 2016 Summer Olympics.

  Réflexion

Research how handball is played. Which popular sport where you live is it most like? How is it different?

Activité 11

  Qu'est-ce que j'aime?

Which activity is associated with each person described below? Select the logical option.

1. Je suis le capitaine de l'équipe de foot de Paris Saint Germain. J'aime _____ au foot.
   a. manger   b. parler   c. jouer

2. Je suis un élève au Collège LaSalle à Montréal. J'aime _____ la biologie.
   a. habiter   b. étudier   c. dessiner

3. Je suis la chanteuse célèbre québécoise Céline Dion. Je suis bilingue. J'aime _____ en français et en anglais.
   a. lire   b. travailler   c. chanter

4. Je suis bénévole à l'UNICEF. J'aime _____ dans ma communauté.
   a. travailler   b. écouter   c. danser

5. J'aime *Roméo et Juliette* et *Hamlet*. J'aime _____ les pièces de Shakespeare.
   a. dormir   b. lire   c. peindre

6. Je suis sociable. J'aime _____ avec des amis.
   a. discuter   b. manger   c. voyager

Réflexion interculturelle

 What are the most popular sports in your region? Are there any sports that are popular in your region, Quebec and France?

Reflect back on the video blogs from Marianne and François. In which sports do you or the bloggers participate? Describe some similarities and differences about sports at your school, in Quebec, and in France. Answer the questions in the discussion forum in Explorer.

> **Mon progrès interculturel**
>
> I can identify popular sports in Quebec and France and how they are similar to or different from sports in my community.

Activité 12

Les activités préférées des Français

Les 10 principaux loisirs des Français

1. Surfer sur internet
2. Regarder la télévision
3. Voir des amis, la famille
4. Écouter la musique
5. Aller au cinéma
6. Jouer aux sports
7. Cuisiner
8. Faire des activités culturelles
9. Lire
10. Faire du shopping

Berne, Suisse

Étape 1: Demandez et répondez

Read the infographic and infer meaning of words you do not know. Then, ask a *partenaire* whether he or she likes or dislikes the activities listed.

Modèle

Élève A: Est-ce que tu aimes lire?

Élève B: Oui, j'aime lire./Non, je n'aime pas lire.

> **Mon progrès communicatif**
>
> I can ask and answer questions about activities that I like and dislike.

Étape 2: Comparez

Compare your answers from *Étape 1*. Which pastimes do you share with your *partenaire*?

Modèle

Je suis comme François parce que j'aime…

Découvrons 2

Expressing Preferences

> Salut! Est-ce que **tu aimes** écouter de la musique classique?

> Non, **je n'aime pas** écouter de la musique classique.

> Oui, **j'aime** beaucoup la musique moderne.

Découvertes

▶◄ ✦ Read the dialogue and notice the words in bold. What do you observe about the different forms? Can you figure out when to use **j'aime** and **tu aimes**? Discuss with classmates and teacher, view the **Découvrons 2** resources for this unit online in Explorer, and check the **Synthèse de grammaire** at the end of this unit.

Activité 13

Vingt questions: Quelles activités aimes-tu?

✍ Étape 1: Écrivez

Look at these words. Select and write five (5) activities you like to do. Don't let anyone see your words!

Activités

manger des hamburgers/salades	jouer aux jeux vidéo
jouer au foot/basket/volley/tennis	étudier
lire	écrire
travailler dans ma communauté	peindre
parler français	passer du temps avec des amis
jouer de la guitare/du piano	chanter
discuter	…

💬 Étape 2: Demandez et répondez

Work with a **partenaire**. Ask and answer questions like the ones in the model. Include some of the **Expressions utiles** to react to your partner's answers.

Modèle

Élève A: Émilie, est-ce que tu aimes jouer de la guitare?

Élève B: Oui, j'aime ça.

Élève A: Ah, tu es musicienne. C'est super!

Élève A: Jacques, est-ce que tu aimes jouer au hockey?

Élève B: Non, je n'aime pas ça.

Élève A: Ah, tu n'es pas athlète.

Détail grammatical

Les questions avec est-ce que

Est-ce que is a quick and easy tool used to phrase questions in French. When you see it at the beginning of a question, it means that it's a yes or no question.

Par exemple:
The question: **Est-ce que tu aimes le chocolat?**
Can be answered either by:
Oui! J'aime le chocolat!
Or: **Non, je n'aime pas le chocolat.**

You will soon learn other ways that it can be used to phrase questions.

Expressions utiles

Réactions

You can react and express interest in what people tell you in French by using the following expressions.

C'est intéressant!
That's interesting!

C'est super!
That's great!

Moi aussi!
Me too!

Moi non plus!
Me neither!

Très bien!
Very good!

Mon progrès communicatif

I can identify key words and some information in an online ad for a summer camp.

Activité 14

Les activités d'été

Étape 1: Lisez et écrivez

You are searching for a summer camp in France. Look for different activities on this advertisement for a French summer camp. Make a list of activities that you like and don't like to do. Practice writing simple sentences using *J'aime* and *Je n'aime pas* + the activity.

Saint-Yrieix-la-Perche

SPORT ACADEMY

Un mot d'ordre pour ce séjour : le sport ! Notre Sport Academy pose ses valises à Saint-Yrieix-la-Perche dans un complexe dédié exclusivement aux sports ! Pas moins de 7 stages sportifs vous sont proposés ! Un concept unique en son genre que vous ne serez pas prêts oublier.

Colonies de vacances

DATES DES SÉJOURS

Toussaint 2017
22-28 octobre
29 octobre – 4 novembre

Printemps 2018
15-21 avril

7-10 11-13 14-17 ÂGE | TRAIN | CENTRE DE VACANCES | SALLE INFORMATIQUE

INFORMATIONS PRATIQUES

ACTIVITÉS COMPLÉMENTAIRES • Sports collectifs, piscine, jeux de société, jeux vidéo...

SOIRÉES • Structures gonflables dans la piscine, quiz musical, visionnage des grands moments sportifs en fonction du stage choisi, disco, jeux, DVD...

HÉBERGEMENT • Les jeunes sont logés à Saint-Yrieix-la-Perche. Les jeunes sont logés dans des chambres de 1 à 4 lits. Pension complète, les repas sont pris dans le restaurant du centre. Les infrastructures sportives se trouvent sur place ou à proximité. Centre aquatique.

VOYAGE • Train accompagné Paris-Limoges puis transfert en autocar privé. Préacheminement des villes de province.

 38

À choisir au moment de l'inscription

TENNIS ACADEMY

POUR LES MORDUS DE TENNIS
15 heures/semaine. Encadrées par des moniteurs brevet d'État. Le stage se déroule au club de Saint-Yrieix sur 3 courts couverts et 1 court extérieur. Vous travaillez les bases technico-tactiques dans des groupes de niveau. Travail au panier, exercices à thème, matches dirigés, tournoi. Chaque séance débute par des échauffements physiques. Une séance vidéo est organisée durant le stage pour étudier votre progression.

BASKET ACADEMY

UN OBJECTIF, LE ALL STAR GAME !
15 heures/semaine. Encadrées par des moniteurs brevet d'État. Travail sur des ateliers : technique individuelle offensive et défensive (shoot, passe, dribble, déplacement, marquage et démarquage), apprentissage des formations tactiques. Matches à thème, All-Star Game, concours...

FOOTBALL ACADEMY

POUR NE PLUS ÊTRE HORS JEU !
15 heures/semaine. Encadrées par des moniteurs brevet d'État. Travail sur des ateliers : technique individuelle offensive et défensive (tir, passe, contrôle, déplacement, marquage et démarquage), apprentissage des formations tactiques. Matches à thème, tournoi, concours, séance vidéo...

Une question ?
0145309191

♥ **j'aime**

⊘ **je n'aime pas**

Étape 2: Comparez

Compare your list with a ***partenaire*** by asking questions if they like or dislike a specific activity. Which activities do you both enjoy? Which activities do you both dislike?

Étape 3: Écrivez

Write three summary sentences about your conversation from ***Étape 2***. Use the model below, but don't forget to add in the name of your ***partenaire*** and the activity. Share your findings in a discussion forum in Explorer.

Modèle
....

Je suis comme _____ (nom du/de la partenaire) parce que j'aime _____.

Je ne suis pas comme _____ (nom du/de la partenaire) parce que je n'aime pas _____.

Étape 4: Comparez et écrivez

Using the same format as ***Étape 3***, write sentences comparing yourself with Marianne and François. Watch the video blogs again and take a few notes to help you with your writing and then submit your sentences in Explorer.

Mon progrès communicatif

I can write simple sentences about myself and activities that I like and I don't like.

Activité 15

  Préparons-nous pour les colonies de vacances!

Imagine that you will spend time at a summer camp in France or Quebec. In order to make the best choice of which camp to attend, communicating with a camp director is a wise move. In this activity, you will play the role of a prospective camper who is providing information to the French-speaking camp director, who has requested you to leave this information on his or her voicemail. You must answer in short, but complete sentences in French. Here is a list of information that must be provided in this recording:

- your name
- age
- birthday

- where you are from
- likes
- dislikes

Modèle

Je m'appelle Paul Carson. J'ai 17 ans. Mon anniversaire est le 22 mai. Je suis de Chicago. J'aime parler français et j'aime aussi jouer au football. Je n'aime pas regarder les films.

Mon progrès communicatif

I can introduce myself and provide some basic information about my identity.

Rabat, Maroc

Prononciation

 Le son /e/

One of the most common sounds that you will encounter in French is the sound equivalent to the English combination "ay," as in the words "day" and "say," but stopping the word before arriving at the point where the "y" is pronounced, making the sound shorter. Let's take a look at at a variety of French words with combination of letters and accents that produce that sound.

The first example is the letter e with the accent aigu = *é*. Words that feature this accented "e" include the following:

café   *fiancée*

matinée   *élève*

enchanté

A second example of French spelling that produces that same sound are words that end in the letters *-ez*. There are a number of classroom commands with which you are familiar that end in this combination that include the following:

écoutez   *répétez*

parlez   *regardez*

You will encounter verbs that have the *-ez* ending throughout your studies of French.

There is a third group of French words that also produce the same sound. The majority of French verbs end in the letters *er* in their most basic form, which is called the infinitive. Here is a small list of some of those verbs:

parler = *to speak*   **voyager** = *to travel*

danser = *to dance*   **discuter** = *to discuss*

téléphoner = *to phone*

We don't want to forget some of the months that we have learned that would include the following:

janvier

février

Words that end in *-et* also have that similar sound:

ballet

juillet

et

Partager sa chambre

You have selected the perfect summer camp to attend. Now, you just have to pick a roommate for your cabin.

 Étape 1: Lisez et écrivez

Look at the notes posted on the camp website by four possible roommates to find out about their interests. Select the one most compatible with you. Copy the phrases that indicate things you have in common.

Étape 2: Écrivez

Write a note to the student you have chosen to be your roommate. Introduce yourself and include the following information. You can use your notes in *Étape 1* as a model.

- Your name
- Your age (*j'ai ____ ans*)
- Origin (where you are from)
- Three things you like to do.
- Three things you don't like to do.

Mon progrès communicatif

I can write simple sentences about myself and activities that I like and I don't like.

Salut! Je m'appelle Isabelle Gagnon. J'habite à Montréal, au Canada. J'ai quinze ans et j'aime passer du temps avec des amis, discuter et aller au cinéma.

Je n'aime pas peindre, écrire des poèmes ou étudier.

Salut! Je m'appelle Omar Kacemi. J'habite à Agadir, au Maroc. J'ai quatorze ans et j'aime beaucoup surfer sur internet, jouer à des jeux vidéo et dormir.

Je n'aime pas jouer de la musique, jouer au sport ou chanter.

Bonjour! Je m'appelle Nicolas Dubois et j'ai dix-sept ans. J'habite à Pau, en France. J'aime beaucoup lire, jouer au foot et écouter de la musique.

Je n'aime pas dessiner, travailler ou manger des légumes.

Bonjour! Je m'appelle Malika Dallier. J'ai quinze ans. J'habite à Saint-François, en Guadeloupe. J'aime beaucoup habiter en Guadeloupe et voyager en Haïti.

Je n'aime pas peindre, regarder des films ou jouer au basket, mais j'aime beaucoup jouer au foot.

Mon progrès communicatif

I can write simple sentences about myself and activities that I like and I don't like.

Mon progrès communicatif

I can introduce myself and provide some basic information about my identity.

J'avance 2

Je me présente

You have decided to compete for a state-wide scholarship to help fund the cost of going to a Francophone country as part of an exchange program. In order to introduce yourself to the scholarship committee (made up of French teachers), you need to prepare a video presentation that you can use to introduce yourself.

Étape 1: Écrivez

You have learned that previous applicants have used many tools for visual support in their videos and you need to choose which you will use for your presentation. The options are as follows:

- multimedia presentation
- poster
- photo book or collage

In your presentation tool, be sure to incorporate pictures, drawings or symbols to illustrate and support written statements about yourself including:

- your name
- age
- birthday
- where you are from
- likes
- dislikes

Étape 2: Parlez

Now that you have the support of a presentation tool, you are ready to make a video to introduce yourself to the committee. The narration of your video presentation should consist of a minimum of eight sentences incorporating all the information in your presentation tool. All of the materials for **J'avance 2** can be found in Explorer.

Comment dit-on? 3

✦ Questions et réponses

Comment t'appelles-tu? —Je m'appelle Christine.

Comment ça va? —Ça va bien.

D'où viens-tu? —Je viens de Chicago.

Quelle est la date? —C'est le 15 septembre.

C'est **quand** ton anniversaire? —C'est le 27 août.

Quel âge as-tu? —J'ai 15 ans.

Est-ce que tu es élève? —Oui, je suis élève.

Qu'*est-ce que* tu aimes étudier? —J'aime étudier le français et les cultures (f. pl.) francophones.

Pourquoi *est-ce que* tu étudies le français? —Parce que j'aime voyager au Canada.

Tu parles bien français! **Qui** est ton professeur? —Monsieur Leclerc est mon professeur.

La vieille ville de Montréal

Activité 17

Questions en conversation

🎧 ✦ Étape 1: Écoutez

Listen to Marianne and her friend ask each other some of the questions above. See if you can figure out what the questions and answers are in their conversation.

💬 ✦ Étape 2: Parlez

Now it's your turn. Find a ***partenaire*** and have a similar conversation by asking and answering basic questions. Record a video of your conversation in your Explorer course.

Détail grammatical

L'ordre des mots dans les questions

As you continue to study French, you will see questions that might look different from the ones you've used so far. There is a lot of flexibility in French to switch the word order in questions. However, you will generally see all the same important question words, so pay attention to the question word (who, what, when, where, why, how, how much, how many, which) and the action.

Look at these other questions and see if you can figure out what they are asking:

- **Qu'**aimes-tu étudier?

- Tu as **quel** âge?

- Tu t'appelles **comment**?

- **Quand** est-ce que tu voyages, en général?

- Tu viens d'**où**?

- **Pourquoi** est-ce que tu aimes la musique classique?

- Tu préfères **qui** comme chanteur?

Activité 18

  Conversations avec de nouveaux amis

Match the questions on the left with the logical answers on the right.

Conversation avec Camille

1. Comment t'appelles-tu?

    a. Oui, je suis élève au lycée Montaigne.

2. D'où viens-tu?

    b. J'aime étudier la science.

3. *Est-ce que* tu es élève?

    c. Je m'appelle Camille.

4. Qu'*est-ce que* tu aimes étudier?

    d. C'est le 23 novembre.

5. Quelle est la date?

    e. Je suis de Montréal.

Conversation avec André

1. Comment ça va?

    a. Parce que j'aime les cultures francophones.

2. C'est quand ton anniversaire?

    b. Ça va comme ci comme ça.

3. Quel âge as-tu?

    c. C'est le 17 juillet.

4. Pourquoi *est-ce que* tu étudies le français?

    d. Madame Simard est mon professeur.

5. Qui est ton professeur?

    e. J'ai 14 ans.

Oran, Algeria

Activité 19

   Réponses possibles

You will hear a series of questions asked in French. For each of the eight questions, there will be one appropriate response that you will select from the three choices offered. Mark the correct letter in the column on the right.

	A	B	C	
1.	Je m'appelle Zoë.	C'est le premier avril.	Je suis artiste.	
2.	Ça va mal.	Oui, j'adore jouer au hockey.	Je suis de Québec.	
3.	Je suis de Gaspé.	Je suis musicien.	Monsieur Boucher.	
4.	C'est le 8 février.	Je suis poète.	J'ai 17 ans.	
5.	Je suis du Canada.	Je suis élève.	Ça va très bien!	
6.	J'aime la musique.	J'aime jouer au football.	Je suis blogueur.	
7.	C'est le 30 janvier.	Je m'appelle Georges.	Je parle français et anglais.	
8.	Monsieur Tremblay	J'ai 16 ans.	J'aime lire.	

Activité 20

Entretien

Write down five questions in French that will allow you to find out interesting information about your classmates. Then interview each other to get to know each other better. Keep practicing until you can ask and answer questions confidently. Then, record your interview in your Explorer course.

Modèle

Élève A: Quel âge as-tu?

Élève B: J'ai seize ans.

Élève A: Tu aimes quelles activités?

Élève B: J'aime jouer au football et chanter.

Je vois: Muse is performing on July 16.

Je pense: There are a lot of interesting concerts.

Je me demande: What would I see on social media about this festival?

Activité 21

Le festival d'été de Québec

Étape 1: Lisez et écrivez

Look at the poster for *Le festival d'été de Québec* and fill in the *organisateur en forme d'Y* (Y-chart) making sure to think about the answers to a variety of questions (who, what, where, when, why). After filling in your chart, compare your answers with a *partenaire* and add to your chart based on your discussion.

FESTIVAL D'ÉTÉ DE QUÉBEC (2017), "50 FESTIVAL D'ÉTÉ DE QUÉBEC". Retrieved from [http://tinyurl.com/yacyq2qj].

Étape 2: Lisez

Complete the table below using the poster from *Étape 1* to find five unfamiliar artists. Then use other resources to learn more about them. Make sure to note where you found the information and that it is a reputable source. Go to your Explorer course for the graphic organizer.

Les Cowboys Fringants

nom d'artiste	genre de musique	nationalité	langues utilisées	ressource(s)
Les Cowboys Fringants	*folk*	*canadiens*	*français*	*www.cowboysfringants.com*

  ## Étape 3: Répondez

Choose one artist from *Étape 2* and research their life in depth and listen to their music. Share your answers in a discussion forum in Explorer.

1. How does their identity influence their music? What can you learn about their life from their art?

2. Do you like their music? Why or why not?

Réflexion interculturelle

Using the *diagramme de Venn* in Explorer, compare a music festival or concert in your region to the *Festival d'été de Québec*. What is the same and what is different about the two events? Provide the information requested and answer the questions in the discussion forum in Explorer.

 Mon progrès interculturel

I can identify musical events and musicians in a Francophone region and how they are the same or different from those in my community.

Découvrons 3

Asking and Answering Questions

> Bonjour! Comment **t'appelles-tu**?

> **Je** m'appelle Jacques.

> **Tu** as quel âge?

> **J'**ai 7 ans.

> D'où viens-**tu**?

> **Je** viens de Montréal.

> C'est intéressant! **Tu** parles quelles langues?

> **Je** parle trois langues: le français et l'anglais et j'étudie l'espagnol à l'école.

> C'est impressionnant!

> Qu'est-ce que **tu aimes** étudier?

> **J'aime** étudier le français et les cultures francophones.

> Pourquoi est-ce que **tu étudies** le français?

> Parce que **j'aime** voyager au Canada.

Découvertes

📹 ✦ Read the dialogues and notice the words in bold used to ask and answer questions. What do you observe about the different forms? Do you notice any patterns? Discuss with classmates and your teacher. View the *Découvrons 3* resources for this unit in Explorer and check the *Synthèse de grammaire* at the end of this unit.

Activité 22

💬 Un sondage: Quel âge as-tu?

Are you and your classmates the same age? Ask five of them this question to find out.

Modèle

Élève A: Quel âge as-tu?

Élève B: J'ai 14 ans. Et toi?

Élève A: J'ai 15 ans.

Élève A: Quel âge as-tu?

Élève B: J'ai 15 ans. Et toi?

Élève A: Moi aussi!

Activité 23

✎ 📖 ✦ Informations pratiques

It is a new school year and your French teacher asks you to answer the following questions to learn more about you. Write your answers using complete sentences.

1. Comment t'appelles-tu?

2. Tu as quel âge?

3. D'où viens-tu?

4. C'est quand ton anniversaire?

5. Tu parles quelles langues?

6. Quelles activités aimes-tu?

7. Pourquoi est-ce que tu étudies le français?

Détail grammatical

Est-ce que

Earlier, you learned that when **est-ce que** is placed at the beginning of a question, it indicates that it is a yes or no question. When **est-ce que** is placed after a question word, it should be followed by the subject and then the verb.

Par exemple:

Pourquoi est-ce que tu aimes chanter?

Quand est-ce que tu aimes jouer au basket?

Activité 24

Quelles langues est-ce que tu parles?

💬 Étape 1: Demandez et répondez

Is your class multilingual? Learning a language takes practice and sometimes classes to help you understand how to read, write, speak, and understand.

Ask your classmates questions to find out what languages they speak. Follow the model and include appropriate expressions such as *c'est intéressant!*, *c'est super!*, *moi aussi!*, or *moi non plus!* to acknowledge your classmates' answer.

Modèle

Élève A: Est-ce que tu parles italien?

Élève B: Non, je ne parle pas italien.

Élève A: Ah, _____.

Élève A: Est-ce que tu parles anglais?

Élève B: Oui, je parle anglais.

Élève A: _____.

📖 💬 ✳️ **Étape 2: Regardez**

It is common for young people to learn multiple languages in many countries. Look at this poster for language classes in France and organize your observations in an ***organisateur en forme d'Y***. Consider the questions: ***qui?***, ***quand?***, ***où?***, ***pourquoi?*** and ***comment?*** while filling in the graphic organizer. Then, discuss your observations with a ***partenaire*** and add to your chart based on your discussion.

COURS de LANGUES
organisés par le
Centre de Formation Plurilingue

Débutant · Intermédiaire · Avancé · Communication commerciale

italien
français
russe
anglais
turc
espagnol
chinois
allemand

lundi, mardi, mercredi, jeudi, vendredi:
de 15h30 à 20h30

HORAIRE

samedi
de 14h00 à 16h00
et de 17h30-19h30

dimanche
de 10h à 11h30
et de 13h à 14h30

Sessions cours du soir
3 février: anglais / turc
28 avril: russe / français
21 juillet: chinois / anglais
13 octobre: italien / allemand

C F P **Plus d'informations**
22 avenue du Maghreb Arabe 7000 Nabeul - Tunisie
Tél : 72 245 569 | Courriel : info@cfp.com | Web:www.cfp-formation.com

On peut aussi dire

Tu parles quelles langues?

Here are the names of some other languages you may have heard. Add to the list any other languages you or your friends speak or want to learn more about.

allemand	langues des signes
anglais	néerlandais
arabe	polonais
chinois	polonais
créole	portugais
espagnol	vietnamien
italien	

Je vois…
Je pense…
Je me demande…

La rue Petit Champlain dans la basse-ville de Québec.

 ✦ **Les langues et l'identité**

Look at the charts and decide whether the statements are true (***vrai***) or false (***faux***). If they are false, change them to be true.

1. 51% des Français parlent deux langues.

2. 25% des Canadiens sont bilingues en français et anglais.

3. Il y a plus de (*more*) Canadiens bilingues que de Français bilingues.

4. Plus de Canadiens parlent anglais que français.

5. 6% des Français parlent trois langues étrangères.

Langues parlées par les Canadiens et les Français

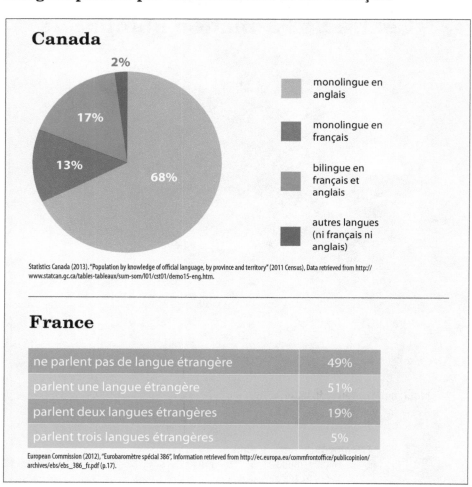

Canada

- 2% — monolingue en anglais
- 17% — monolingue en français
- 13% — bilingue en français et anglais
- 68% — autres langues (ni français ni anglais)

Statistics Canada (2013). "Population by knowledge of official language, by province and territory" (2011 Census), Data retrieved from http://www.statcan.gc.ca/tables-tableaux/sum-som/l01/cst01/demo15-eng.htm.

France

ne parlent pas de langue étrangère	49%
parlent une langue étrangère	51%
parlent deux langues étrangères	19%
parlent trois langues étrangères	5%

European Commission (2012), "Eurobaromètre spécial 386", Information retrieved from http://ec.europa.eu/commfrontoffice/publicopinion/archives/ebs/ebs_386_fr.pdf (p.17).

Zoom culture

Perspective culturelle: L'identité linguistique du Québec

  Connexions

What do you already know about the history of Quebec? Do you think that French was always the official language of Quebec?

In 1608 when Samuel de Champlain founded the city of Quebec, the explorers brought not only supplies, but their language and culture to the New World. The language, however, began to evolve as explorers used maritime expressions in daily life (***embarquer/débarquer de la voiture***). The French colonists also interacted with native populations, including the Algonquin and Mohawk peoples, who introduced new words like ***caribou*** *(deer; elk)* and ***toboggan*** *(sled, luge)*.

When France ceded the vast majority of its North American territory to Great Britain in 1763, there was a major linguistic and cultural transition as now these people were no longer French, but British. There were decades of discrimination and fighting to maintain the French language and culture. Finally, in 1977, ***La Charte de la langue française*** was passed into law, which decreed French as Quebec's only official language. This law, commonly known as Bill 101, gives Francophones the right to communicate in French at work.

  Réflexion

What role did the French people and language play in the origins of the United States? Why is French an important language of communication in North America and across the world?

Château Frontenac vu de la Basse-Ville du Vieux Québec.

Réflexion interculturelle

⟲ 👥 ✦ What languages have you heard in the media or spoken in your home, school or community? In what context do you hear or see each language?

What do you know about the linguistic diversity in your region? Search for some statistics to verify or correct your assumptions.

Provide the information requested or answer the questions in the discussion forum in Explorer.

✦ **Mon progrès interculturel**

I can identify other languages spoken in my community and what they represent to people.

J'avance 3

Le nouvel élève

🎧 📝 ✳️ Étape 1: Écoutez et écrivez

You will hear a dialogue between a newly arrived Francophone exchange student and his bilingual school counselor at a high school. Look at the grid below, listen for the required information, and fill in the spaces. If information is not shared in the conversation, leave the box blank.

	nom *(name)*	origine	âge	anniversaire	sports
l'élève					
le conseiller					

📝 ⭕⭕ ✳️ Étape 2: Comparez et écrivez

How is the student in the dialogue similar and/or different from you and other students at your school? Identify at least two ways that you are similar and/or different from Olivier.

Mon progrès communicatif

I can understand information related to identity and preferences.

Mon progrès interculturel

I can identify some similarities and differences between Francophone young people and myself.

🗨 ✦ Étape 3: Demandez et répondez

Your school television station that broadcasts school news and events each morning is producing a feature on one of the visiting Francophone students. You will work in pairs and record an interview where both the host student and the visiting student (your ***partenaire*** and you) will ask each other questions. Use the list below as a guide to the nature of the questions that should be asked and answered. Each of you will ask three of the six questions and respond to the questions from your ***partenaire***. Work together to ensure that together you ask all six questions.

Nature of questions
Name
Age
Place of origin
Likes and dislikes
Birthday
How he or she is doing

All of the materials for ***J'avance 3*** can be found in Explorer.

✦ **Mon progrès communicatif**

I can ask and answer questions to get to know another person.

📶 📶 📶

Reims, France

Synthèse de grammaire

1. Expressing Who I am: *le verbe être et les adjectifs*

In this unit, you have seen three forms of the verb *être* (to be); all the present tense forms of this verb are given below:

	singular one person		plural two or more persons	
the speaker **him or herself**	je	suis	nous	sommes
the person spoken **to**	tu (*informal*)	es	vous (*formal or informal*)	êtes
	vous (*formal*)*	êtes		
the person or people spoken **about**	il	est	ils	sont
	elle	est	elles	sont

*The versatile subject pronoun **vous** may refer to either one person or any number of people since it can be found in both the singular and plural columns in the chart above. **Vous**, when referring to a singular person, has a formal tone as opposed to the word **tu**, which is used to reference someone informally, like a brother, sister or good friend. Use **vous** to refer to a teacher or an adult neighbor. For future reference, when you encounter a verb conjugation chart like the one above, **vous** will be located only on the plural side of those charts, no matter if it would be plural or singular, formal or informal.

The verb *être* can be used with adjectives to describe a person's identity:

— **Tristan est sérieux**.

   Tristan is serious.

— **Carole est sérieuse**.

   Carole is serious.

2. Expressing Preferences: *j'aime/tu aimes*

In French, you can ask about a friend's likes and dislikes by using **Est-ce que tu aimes** ____?, with the infinitive form of a verb **(-er, -ir, -re)** in the blank. To answer the question, use **J'aime** ____.

To express what you do not like, use **Je n'aime pas** _____.

—**Est-ce que tu aimes étudier?**
Do you like to study?

—**Oui, j'aime étudier, mais je n'aime pas écrire.**
Yes, I like to study, but I do not like to write.

For many verbs in French, the form used for *je* ends in **-e** and the form used for *tu* ends in **-es**. You will learn other verbs that will have a different pattern.

3. Asking and Answering Questions: *questions et réponses*

Questions with a yes/no answer in French can be created in different ways:

- You can use the regular word order of a sentence and simply make it a question by using rising intonation, with the tone of your voice sounding higher at the end.

  Tu parles français?

- Also, you can attach the question marker **est-ce que** to the beginning of a sentence, which signals the listener that what is to follow is a question.

  Est-ce que tu parles français?

- Another way to make a question is to switch the order of the subject and the verb in the sentence. A regular sentence in French has the subject first and then the verb. Using the verb first and the subject second (with a dash in between) will make the sentence into a question.

  Parles-tu français?

Information questions (in contrast to yes/no questions) require a question word or phrase (*qui, que, où, quand, pourquoi, comment, quel(le)(s)*). Sometimes you will see **est-ce que** after a question word as in the following examples:

  Pourquoi est-ce que tu aimes chanter?

  Quand est-ce que tu aimes jouer au basket?

Vocabulaire

Comment dit-on? 1: I can talk about who I am.

Qui suis-je?	*Who am I?*
américain/américaine	*American*
un/une artiste	*artist*
un/une athlète	*athlete*
bilingue	*bilingual*
un chanteur/une chanteuse	*singer*
un/une élève	*student*
un musicien/une musicienne	*musician*
sérieux/sérieuse	*serious*
sportif/sportive	*athletic*

Comment dit-on? 2: I can express my likes and dislikes.

Mes activités préférées	*My favorite activities*
aller au café, cinéma	*to go to a cafe, movie theater*
danser	*to dance*
dessiner	*to draw*
écouter de la musique	*to listen to music*
étudier	*to study*
jouer au sport	*to play a sport*
jouer de la musique	*to play music*
lire	*to read*
manger	*to eat*
passer du temps avec des amis	*to spend time with friends*
regarder une série, un film	*to watch a show, film*
surfer sur internet	*to surf the Internet, web*

Comment dit-on? 3: I can ask and answer questions to get to know another person.

Mots interrogatifs	*Question words*
Comment?	*How?*
Où?, D'où?	*Where?, From where?*
Pourquoi?	*Why?*
Quand?	*When?*
Que, Qu'?	*What?*
Quel(le)?	*Which? What?*
Qui?	*Who?*
C'est quand ton anniversaire?	*When is your birthday?*
Comment ça va?	*How are you?*
Comment t'appelles-tu?	*What's your name?*
D'où viens-tu?	*Where do you come from?*
Est-ce que tu es élève?	*Are you a student?*
Pourquoi est-ce que tu étudies le français?	*Why do you study French?*
Qu'est-ce que tu aimes étudier?	*What do you like to study?*
Quel âge as-tu?	*How old are you?*
Quelle est la date?	*What is the date?*
Qui est ton professeur?	*Who is your teacher?*

Quelles langues est-ce que tu parles?		
Which languages do you speak?		
allemand	*German*	
anglais	*English*	
arabe	*Arabic*	
chinois	*Chinese*	
créole	*Creole*	
espagnol	*Spanish*	
italien	*Italian*	
langue des signes	*Sign language*	
néerlandais	*Dutch*	
polonais	*Polish*	
portugais	*Portuguese*	
vietnamien	*Vietnamese*	

Expressions utiles	*Useful expressions*
Très bien!	*Very good!*
C'est super!	*That's great!*
C'est intéressant!	*That's interesting!*
Moi aussi!	*Me too!*
Moi non plus!	*Me neither!*

J'y arrive

Questions essentielles

- How do I exchange information about my identity and that of others?
- What are cultural similarities and differences between myself and others in a Francophone community?

Un échange scolaire

Your school has been chosen to participate in an exchange program bringing students from Quebec or France to your community. You have volunteered to host one of the students in your home for three weeks. Before you begin, refer to the *J'y arrive* rubric in Explorer to familiarize yourself with the evaluation criteria.

Interpretive Assessment

Qui sont les élèves étrangers?

Get acquainted with François and Marianne, two of the exchange students, by watching the video blogs they have sent to your school.

▶ ✦ Étape 1: Regardez

Watch the video blogs of François and Marianne. Using the graphic organizer in Explorer, mark the words you hear. Compare your list with the list of a *partenaire*.

▶ ✦ Étape 2: Regardez

Watch the video blogs again to learn everything you can about François and Marianne. In Explorer, note what you learn in the organizer.

▶ ✎ ✦ Étape 3: Identifiez

Using the checklist in Explorer, identify the characteristics of each video blogger.

Based on what the two students said in their video blogs, which traits of these students would make you more likely to host him/her in your home during the three week stay in your community?

Interpersonal Assessment

  E–mail: Je me présente

Write an email to introduce yourself to one of the exchange students, following the instructions in Explorer.

Presentational Assessment

  Étape 1: Présentez

You will create a video blog to share with the family with whom you will stay when you and your classmates travel to Quebec or France next summer. Follow the directions in Explorer to create and share your video.

   **Étape 2: Comparez**

Of the two video bloggers you have met in this unit, who is the most similar to you? Copy and complete the sentences and share with a *partenaire* in the discussion forum in Explorer.

UNITÉ 2
À l'école

Objectifs de l'unité

Exchange information about your life at school, including people, places, schedules, and student activities.

Interpret images, videos, and schedules to gain insights into what school life is like in a Francophone country.

Present information about your own life at school.

Investigate elements of school life and aspects of time in Francophone cultures.

⊕ Questions essentielles

How is student life at my school similar to and/or different from student life in a Francophone country?

How do courses and schedules reflect the educational values of a community?

What places, people, and activities define student life?

When you meet young people who speak French, you will want to talk about your life at school. In this unit, Hamid will share his school experiences in Algeria through his video blogs. Learning about schools and education in other cultures will help you understand how to make students new to your community feel comfortable in your school.

Rencontre interculturelle

L'Algérie

L'Algérie est un pays d'Afrique du Nord bordé par la mer Méditerranée. Après une période de colonisation française, l'Algérie proclame son indépendance en 1962. C'est le plus grand pays du continent africain.

Les langues officielles de l'Algérie sont l'arabe et le berbère. Le français est une langue importante en Algérie pour l'éducation et le commerce. La majorité de la population algérienne parle ou comprend le français.

Nom: Hamid

Langues parlées: arabe, français, allemand, anglais, japonais

Origine: Alger, Algérie

L'Algérie et le continent africain

Le nord de l'Afrique et la mer Méditerranée

Alger, la capitale algérienne

Le désert du Sahara en Algérie

Alger, Algérie

Je m'appelle Hamid.

Je passe en deuxième année secondaire, classe scientifique.

J'aime jouer aux jeux vidéo et jouer du piano.

J'étudie la biologie.

Hamid est élève au lycée El Macir à Alger, la capitale de l'Algérie. Il est en deuxième année secondaire. C'est un élève sérieux. Il aime les sciences. Hamid aime aussi la musique. Il joue du piano.

Activité 1

Bonjour, Hamid!

📖 ✦ Étape 1: Préparez

Look at the photo of Hamid and what is in his speech bubbles. What information do you think he has included in his video blog? Can you tell what his interests are for school and extracurricular activities? Write your responses in Explorer.

▶ ✤ Étape 2: Écoutez

Listen to Hamid's video blog recording and place check marks (✔) next to the keywords when you hear them.

écoutez	✔
je m'appelle	
secondaire	
classe scientifique	
biologie	
jouer aux jeux vidéo	
jouer du piano	

▶ ✎ ✤ Étape 3: Résumez

Listen and watch again. In Explorer, write a few sentences about what Hamid is telling us about himself. Include words or sentences from the picture captions and also additional information that you understand and find interesting.

◯◯ ✤ Étape 4: Comparez

How is Hamid similar to you and how is he different from you? Share your comparisons in class and write a few sentences describing these similarities and differences in Explorer.

Modèle

Je suis comme Hamid. J'aime la biologie aussi.

Le port d'Alger, en Algérie

Réflexion interculturelle

◯◯ ✤ What subjects do you study at school? What are are your favorite extracurricular activities? Do you have academic goals for the future? How is Hamid similar to and/or different from you? Answer the questions in the discussion forum in Explorer.

✤ Mon progrès interculturel

I can identify some similarities and differences between a Francophone teen and myself related to school life.

Communiquons

Comment dit-on? 1

✦ Les fournitures scolaires

> *Qu'est-ce qui est nécessaire?*

> *J'ai un sac à dos, mais j'ai besoin de beaucoup de choses.*

Un billet *(bill)* de 1.000 dinars. Le dinar est la monnaie d'Algérie.

Les fournitures scolaires à acheter

feuilles de papier (paquet de 100) **145DZD**

stylos (paquet de 6) **225DZD**

trousse **1.050DZD**

crayons (paquet de 10) **265DZD**

Les crayons coûtent moins chers en paquet.

Le sac à dos coûte mille deux cent cinquante dinars.

sac à dos **1.250DZD**

classeur **260DZD**

livres **1.750 - 6.000DZD**

dictionnaire anglais-français **775DZD**

Les cahiers sont parfaits pour le cours d'anglais.

cahiers (8 x 100 feuilles) **720DZD**

ciseaux **775DZD**

agenda scolaire **535DZD**

calculatrice **860DZD**

La technologie à l'école.

portable **52.000DZD**

tablette **56.000 DZD**

ordinateur **84.000DZD**

Activité 2

▶️ ✴️ Qu'est-ce qu'il y a dans ton sac à dos?

First, read the list of school supplies in the chart below. Then, as you watch the video blogs, indicate which items Marianne, Ariane, and Noah have in their backpacks.

	Marianne	Ariane	Noah
livre			
manuel scolaire			
cahier			
calculatrice			
dictionnaire			
tablette			
trousse			
crayon			
ciseaux			
stylo			

Prononciation

▶️ ✴️ Word Stress in French

In words that have more than one syllable, one of the syllables gets more emphasis than others when pronounced. In the English word "ge*om*etry," notice that the second syllable "om" gets emphasized when it's pronounced. In French, its cognate ***géométrie*** has word stress on the last syllable, "*-trie.*" Whereas English word stress is quite variable, French word stress tends to fall on the last syllable. This can be a handy tip when making a guess at how to pronounce a cognate in French.

Exemples en anglais et en français (the stressed syllable is underlined):

envelope	**enveloppe**
portable	**portable**
calculator	**calculatrice**
apartment	**appartement**
carrot	**carotte**

Comment dit-on?

✴️ Les numéros de 30 à 69

In ***Unité préliminaire***, you learned numbers up to 31 to be able to talk about dates and calendars. The pattern continues as you count from 30–69.

30 trente

31 trente et un

32 trente-deux

33 trente-trois

…

40 quarante

44 quarante-quatre

50 cinquante

57 cinquante-sept

60 soixante

69 soixante-neuf

On peut aussi dire

In your *salle de classe*, you or your teacher might also use or need to talk about the following objects.

un bureau
a desk, an office

une chaise
a chair

un feutre
a marker

un tableau
a whiteboard, chalkboard

un taille-crayon
a pencil sharpener

Activité 3

Qu'est-ce qui est nécessaire?

📝 ⊕ Étape 1: Écrivez

Complete the *Tableau à deux colonnes (T-chart)* with items you already have in your backpack, then use the *liste de fournitures scolaires* to identify items you would need if you were a student at *Lycée Pélégri* in Algiers.

Lycée Pélégri

Liste de fournitures scolaires

☐ 3 stylos   ☐ calculatrice

☐ 4 cahiers   ☐ agenda scolaire

☐ feuilles de papier   ☐ livre

☐ ordinateur   ☐ dictionnaire français-anglais

---

j'ai...	j'ai besoin de/d'...

💬 ⊕ Étape 2: Demandez et répondez

Now ask your *partenaire* if he or she has any of the items that you need, using the *Modèle* to guide you. Note any items that your *partenaire* has in your list.

Modèle

Élève A: As-tu _____?

Élève B: Oui, j'ai _____.

     Non, je n'ai pas de/d' _____.

🎤 ⊕ Étape 3: Présentez

Summarize the information in your chart and share with a small group. Be sure to share an item you have, ask for an item you need, and indicate something that your *partenaire* has or does not have. Be sure to use *il* if your *partenaire* is male and *elle* if your *partenaire* is female.

Modèle

J'ai _____.

J'ai besoin de/d' _____.

Il/Elle a _____.

Il/Elle n'a pas de/d' _____.

Activité 4

⊙⊙ 💬 Qu'est-ce qui coûte plus cher?

Work with a *partenaire* to compare prices of school supplies in Algeria. Ask and answer questions using the ad in *Comment dit-on?* 1.

Modèle

Qu'est-ce qui coûte plus cher: des stylos ou des crayons?

des crayons

1. un ordinateur/une tablette

2. un sac à dos/des ciseaux

3. un agenda scolaire/une calculatrice

4. une trousse/des feuilles de papier

Mon progrès communicatif

I can respond to questions relating to school supplies.

Mon progrès communicatif

I can write a list of school supplies.

Qu'est-ce qu'on utilise à l'école?

✏️ ✦ Étape 1: Préparez

A new student who speaks French needs to get school supplies. Write shopping lists for the items needed in four of your classes. Indicate the quantity of each item needed, as done in the model in the first column.

le cours de français	le cours d'art	le cours de maths	le cours de sciences
un dictionnaire			

✏️ ✦ Étape 2: Écrivez

The new French speaking student for whom you made the list of school supplies in *Étape 1* has remembered that his parents are out shopping and that they could purchase the necessary school items. One problem exists - your friend's cell phone is at home. Using your cell phone, write a text message for your friend advising his parents what to purchase based on the items in the chart in *Étape 1*.

Modèle

J'ai besoin d'un dictionnaire.

Zoom culture

Pratique culturelle: Le système scolaire algérien

  Connexions

What grade levels make up the different schools in your community? How are students grouped together? How is your performance assessed in your classes? How do you discover or check your current grades in each class?

In Algeria, there are three types of schools and students generally start school at the age of 6 in Grade 1. At the end of ***école secondaire-collège***, students are required to take the ***Brevet d'Enseignement Moyen (BEM)***. In ***école secondaire-lycée***, students prepare for the ***Baccalauréat*** exam and must choose to specialize in one of three areas ***(lettres, sciences, technologie).***

Le système scolaire algérien

âge	école	années	
6–11 ans	école primaire	5 ans au total	
11–15 ans	école secondaire - collège	4 ans au total	
15–18 ans	école secondaire - lycée	3 ans au total	Première (1ʳᵉ) année
			Deuxième (2ᵉ) année
			Troisième (3ᵉ) année

The grades that students receive in an Algerian school use the same system as France, but it is quite different from grades in the U.S. The range of grades goes from 1–20 instead of 1–100. Algerian grades that are 13 and higher are generally considered in the "A" range, while grades below 8 are what we would consider unsatisfactory or failing. The chart below shows how the two grading systems compare.

L'Algérie	Les États-Unis	
20–13 (très bien)	A	4
12 (bien)	B+	3
11 (assez bien)	B	3
10 (passable)	C	2
9–8 (médiocre)	D	1
7–0 (faible, très faible, nul)	F	0

In some Francophone countries, it is common for teachers to share student grades in front of the whole class when returning assignments. The grade might also include some feedback and a class ranking. In Algeria, it is common for students to carry a ***cahier de correspondance*** in which teachers can share grades and comments with the student and his or her parents. Major exam scores, like the ***brevet*** and ***baccalauréat*** are often printed in the newspaper and online for everyone to see.

  Réflexion

1. What benefits and/or disadvantages do you notice about the Algerian system?

2. Research another Francophone country's school system and compare it with what you now know about Algeria and the system in your community.

Mon progrès interculturel

I can identify some information about grade levels in a Francophone country and how students' grades are recorded.

Détail grammatical

La possession avec de

The expression *definite article + de + person* is one way to indicate possession:

L'ordinateur de Paul est moderne.
Paul's computer is modern.

Les crayons d'Aurélie sont dans le sac à dos.
Aurélie's pencils are in the backpack.

Note how in French the object possessed comes first, followed by *de* (or *d'* if it precedes a vowel) and then the owner. French does not have a possessive structure like *'s* in English.

Réflexion interculturelle

What are the academic practices or traditions associated with being promoted to the next grade level and/or school in your community? What cultural values are expressed in those celebrations or traditions? Are a student's grades considered private or public? How are grades shared and discussed in your family and in your community?

Answer the questions in the discussion forum in Explorer.

Activité 6

De qui est...?

In groups of four, contribute two items per person from your backpacks to a pile, without looking at who contributed each item. Then, take turns guessing the owner of each item, following the model.

Modèle

Élève A: C'est le stylo de Paul?

Élève B: Oui, c'est le stylo de Paul./Non, c'est le stylo de Sylvie.

Élève C: C'est la calculatrice de Christine?

Élève D: Oui, c'est la calculatrice de Christine./Non, c'est la calculatrice de Jean.

Activité 7

📖 Le sac de qui?

Lina, Omar, and Khaled have each lost something. Read their descriptions of the lost items and match each of the images to the correct owner.

Lina: J'ai perdu *(I lost)* mon ordi et ma tablette! C'est un grand problème. Dans mon sac, il y a aussi une calculatrice et des cahiers.

Omar: Il y a des cahiers et un livre dans le sac que j'ai perdu. Il y a aussi des crayons et une calculatrice. J'ai perdu mon sac dans le bus.

Khaled: Il n'y a pas de livres. Mais, il y a des stylos et une calculatrice dans ma trousse bleue.

Alger, Algérie

Découvrons 1

Identifying People or Things

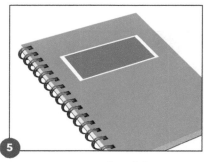
un stylo rouge

une calculatrice moderne

un sac à dos français

des crayons jaunes

un grand cahier

des professeurs aimables

une tablette américaine

Découvertes

In **Découvrons 1,** look at the first word in the caption of each of the above images. What do you observe about the different forms? They all correspond to the English words "a," "an" or "some" **(un, une, des)** and are referred to as indefinite articles. Can you figure out the pattern of when to use each one? Discuss the examples with your classmates and teachers, view the **Découvrons 1** resources for this unit in your Explorer course, and check the **Synthèse de grammaire** at the end of the unit.

Activité 8

Masculin ou féminin?

🎧 **Étape 1: Écoutez**

Listen to your teacher say the following school supplies with the corresponding indefinite articles. Write down the number of the photo in **Découvrons 1** that corresponds to what you hear.

A. _____ B. _____ C. _____ D. _____ E. _____ F. _____

🎧 **Étape 2: Ré-écoutez**

Listen to these words again, paying special attention to the indefinite articles preceding the nouns. Show that you and a partner understand the gender and number of the word by saying it with its indefinite article and pointing to the image: **un** for masculine, **une** for feminine, and **des** for plural. Reminder: The article **des** is the plural for both masculine and feminine.

Activité 9

🗒 ✴ Les fournitures scolaires

You receive a message from our video blogger Hamid, about what he needs for school each day, but there are some words missing. Use logic to determine the missing words.

> Bonjour!
>
> J'ai besoin de/d' _____ (1) calculatrice pour le cours de mathématiques. J'ai (*I have*) _____ (2) grand cahier orange pour le cours d'histoire et je préfère écrire avec _____ (3) stylo bleu. Il y a aussi _____ (4) livres pour le cours de biologie. J'aime utiliser _____ (5) tablette pour le cours de français. Pour le cours d'art, j'ai _____ (6) crayons et _____ (7) ciseaux. Et toi, qu'est-ce que tu utilises à l'école?
>
> Hamid

I can understand when someone names school supplies.

J'avance 1

Dans mon sac à dos

Étape 1: Regardez

Listen to Hamid as he describes what is in his backpack. Using the checklist, check off (✔) the items that Hamid tells us are in his backpack.

Étape 2: Demandez et répondez

You accidentally forgot your backpack on the bus and are asking friends and classmates for at least two items you need to function in your classes today. Record your conversation in Explorer.

Sofia	Your friend greets you as you walk into school.
vous	Greet your friend Sofia and tell her you need a pencil.
Sofia	She doesn't have a pencil, but she offers you a pen.
vous	Respond to her offer and thank her.
Karim	You see your other friend. He greets you and asks how you are doing.
vous	Greet Karim and respond to his question. Tell him another school supply you need.
Karim	He has what you are looking for and gives it to you.
vous	Thank him and say goodbye.

📝 ✦ Étape 3: Décrivez

You still cannot find your backpack that you left on the bus. You must file a report with the office so that if it is found, it can be returned to you. Be sure to include at least four items in your lost backpack.

Nom:

E–mail:

Description de ce qui est perdu (*lost*):

All of the materials for **J'avance 1** can be found in Explorer.

Comment dit-on? 2

✤ Les matières

Horaire	Matière	Salle
8h15-9h55	Physique	30
9h55-10h15	Récré	
10h15-11h05	Mathématiques	cour/préau
11h05-11h55	LV: Espagnol	33
11h55-13h00	Déjeuner	15
13h00-14h40	SVT	restaurant scolaire
14h40-15h30	Informatique	34
15h30-16h20	EPS	37
		gymnase

Horaire	Matière	Salle
8h15-9h55	LV: Anglais	23
9h55-10h15	Récré	cour/préau
10h15-11h05	Français	15
11h05-11h55	Sciences sociales: Histoire-géo	27
11h55-13h00	Déjeuner	restaurant scolaire
13h00-14h40	Littérature	11
14h40-15h30	Musique	10
15h30-16h20	EPS	gymnase

*J'ai le cours de SVT à 13h00 dans la salle de classe 34. J'aime le cours de SVT parce qu'il est **fascinant** et **facile**. Et toi?*

*Pas moi, je n'aime pas le cours de SVT parce qu'il est **difficile**.*

À 15h30 j'ai éducation physique et sportive.

Moi aussi, j'ai EPS à 15h30. Super!

Activité 10

📝 ⦿ ✦ **Classer les activités**

Which classes offered at your school fit into these categories? Write as many as you can in the first row *(dans mon école)*. In the second row, add as many other possibilities as you can. Use the vocabulary from the student schedules in the *Détail linguistique* sidebar or use the *Stratégies* sidebar on the next page.

	sciences sociales	langues	sciences	arts
dans mon école				
dans d'autres écoles				

Activité 11

🎧 **Que fais-tu en cours?**

Look at the two schedules on the smart phones. Listen to your teacher describe activities that take place in the students' classes and say the name of the class and where it takes place. Consider the word bank below while you are listening.

animaux   chanter   numéros   continents   ordinateur   paragraphes   parler   planète   calculs   écrire   élèves   amis

Mon progrès communicatif

I can understand some basic activities and objects related to specific classes.

Détail linguistique

Les abréviations

Students in Francophone countries use these common abbreviations.

éducation physique/sportive ⟶ EPS

géographie ⟶ géo

laboratoire ⟶ labo

langue vivante ⟶ LV

mathématiques ⟶ maths

professeur ⟶ prof

sciences de la vie et de la terre ⟶ SVT

Stratégies

Recognizing Cognates

Learning to recognize cognates will help expand your vocabulary.

les mathématiques ⟶ *mathematics*

la musique ⟶ *music*

les sciences ⟶ *science*

l'algèbre

l'arabe

les arts visuels

la biologie

la chorale

le latin

l'orchestre

la psychologie

le sport (EPS = l'éducation physique et sportive)

Mon progrès communicatif

I can understand the names of classes and how many hours per week they meet.

Activité 12

Les cours de Hamid

▶ ✦ Étape 1: Écoutez

Watch Hamid's video blog and listen carefully as he talks about his classes. Check off (✔) the classes that he currently has from the list in Explorer.

Hamid, il a le cours de/d':

____ physique	____ sport
____ histoire-géo	____ éducation islamique
____ latin	____ orchestre
____ mathématiques	____ arabe
____ SVT	____ biologie
____ sciences naturelles	____ français
____ anglais	____ littérature
____ informatique	____ espagnol

▶ ✦ Étape 2: Réécoutez

Watch Hamid's video blog once again, this time focusing on how many hours a week he has each class. Make a list of his classes (from your selections in *Étape 1*) and next to each, write the number of hours he has that class each week. Record your answers in Explorer. Check your answers with a *partenaire* and watch the video again if there are any discrepancies.

cours de Hamid	nombre d'heures
Modèle mathématiques	6 heures

Activité 13

Quels cours est-ce que tu aimes?

✏ ✵ Étape 1: Choisissez et écrivez

Choose four classes you are currently taking and rank them according to how you feel about them.

–		+	
◄── je n'aime pas ───	j'aime un peu ───	j'aime beaucoup ───	j'adore ──►
Modèle			
les mathématiques	l'histoire	la musique	le français

✏ ✵ Étape 2: Expliquez

Give reasons justifying how you ranked two of your classes.

Modèle
....

J'adore le cours de français parce qu'il est génial.

📱 👫 ✵ Étape 3: Écrivez

You are the mentor of a new student who has arrived at your school. She is going to see the counselor in a few minutes to register for classes. You are writing a couple of suggestions for classes she should take on a sticky note to give to her.

a. Write whether you like a certain class and why so that she can make good course choices.

b. Use different classes than you mentioned in *Étape 2*.

> J'ai... J'aime le cours
> de... d'anglais parce
> parc... qu'il est facile.

On peut aussi dire

Décrivons nos cours

Here are some other adjectives that can be used to describe classes:

amusant	*funny*
fatigant	*tiring*
génial	*awesome*
inspirant	*inspirational*
intéressant	*interesting*

Mon progrès interculturel

I can identify what Francophone students do in their free time at school, where they go, and why.

Détail grammatical

Les articles définis

Quels cours aimes-tu?

J'aime l'anglais.

J'aime la littérature.

J'aime le français.

J'aime les maths.

Notice how, in these examples, class subjects are preceded by either *l', le, la* or *les*. These four words all mean "the" and are called definite articles. *Le* is used before a masculine singular noun, *la* before a feminine singular noun, *l'* before a singular noun (either masculine or feminine) beginning with either an "h" or a vowel, and *les* before any plural noun. In French, there is almost always an article (either definite or indefinite) before a noun.

Zoom culture

Pratique culturelle: La récré

© Jean Gribion, 2017.

Connexion

1. What do you think of when you hear the word "recess"?

2. Where do you typically have recess?

3. How much time do you have daily for recess?

4. Is your recess sometimes affected by weather? If so, what happens to your recess, say for example when it rains?

In France, *la récré* (or *récréation*) is a mandatory part of the school day. In elementary school, students are granted two 20 minute breaks during which time students are free to play outside. Activities such as jump rope, soccer, hop scotch and basketball are very popular during these early years. In middle and high schools, the mandated time is 15 minutes twice a day, during which students may still play individual or group games, but many use the time to socialize with friends. Each school has an outdoor play area called *la cour* where students have *la récré*. Traditionally, schools also have *un préau*, which is a covered area within *la cour* where students can gather when it is raining or snowing.

Réflexion

1. How do these recess times (times when students do not have class) compare to the amount of recess time you have at your school?

2. Do you have an area similar to the *préau* at your school? If so, how does it compare to the French *préau*?

Activité 14

Les cours et les préférences

Étape 1: Parlez

In order to get to know what classes another *élève* in your class is currently taking, ask your *partenaire* which classes he or she has. Ask and answer three questions each.

Modèle

Élève A: Tu as le cours de maths?

Élève B: Oui, j'ai le cours de maths.

Prononciation

 Hard and Soft G Sounds

The letter "g" in French can be pronounced in two ways. The hard "g" sound occurs in the English words "go" and "game." The soft "g" sound occurs in the word "massage" and is the same sound as the "s" in the word "Asia."

Before "a", "o", "u", a "g" in French will be a hard "g." This can occur at the beginning of a word or later in the word.

Exemples:

regarder	bilingue
organiser	langue
gouvernement	

Before "e", "i", or "y", a "g" in French will be a soft "g." This can also occur at the beginning of a word or later in the word.

Exemples:

géo	origine
Algérie	biologie
âge	gymnase

Expressions utiles

Giving reasons why and when

Use **parce que/qu'** (*because*) to give a reason or explanation:

J'aime le cours de français parce qu'il est marrant *(fun)*.

Je n'aime pas le cours de géo parce qu'il est épuisant *(exhausting)*.

pendant la semaine

pendant le week-end

J'aime faire mes devoirs pendant la semaine.

Je n'aime pas faire mes devoirs pendant le week-end.

Étape 2: Expliquez

Then ask a follow-up question about whether he or she likes that class and why.

Élève A: Est-ce que tu aimes le cours d'histoire? Pourquoi?

Élève B: J'aime le cours d'histoire parce qu'il est fascinant.

Mon progrès communicatif

I can ask and answer questions about my class preferences.

Découvrons 2

Telling Time

(Tanger, Maroc)

Il est sept heures trente-six.

07h36

(République Centrafricaine)

Il est dix heures douze.

10h12

(Paris, France)

Il est onze heures quatre.

11h04

(Genève, Suisse)

Il est quinze heures vingt.

15h20

(Besançon, France)

Il est dix-huit heures.

18h00

(Montréal, Canada)

Il est vingt et une heures quarante-cinq.

21h45

Il est vingt-deux heures dix.

22h10

Il est vingt-trois heures cinquante-neuf.

23h59

Découvertes

See **Découvrons 2** and figure out the time of day each image represents. What do you observe about the different forms? While the first three may be more recognizable, the remaining five will pose more of a challenge. This system avoids using the AM/PM system that you are accustomed to using. A hint: Think of time in terms of a 24-hour day to figure out this system. Discuss these new time notations with classmates and your teacher and use the **Découvrons 2** resources found in Explorer as well as the **Synthèse de grammaire** section at the end of this unit.

Quelle heure est-il?

🔍 ⓪ Étape 1: Observez et calculez

Discuss the following questions with a partner.

1. What differences do you see about how the digital times are written and how you usually write them?

2. What is the mathematical equation you do to express the time as it is shown here?

📝 ⓪ ✥ Étape 2: Réfléchissez

What could be the advantages or disadvantages of expressing time as it is here in these photos? Write your answers in the discussion forum in Explorer.

Mon emploi du temps

📝 ♟ ✥ Étape 1: Notez

A new student is going to shadow you until lunch time to learn about your school. Write down your typical morning schedule and share it with this student. Include classes and locations. Record your answers in Explorer.

	cours	où		cours	où
7h00	*l'histoire*	*salle 32*	10h00		
7h30			10h30		
8h00			11h00		
8h30			11h30		
9h00			12h00		
9h30			12h30		

💬 ✳ Étape 2: Demandez et répondez

Work with a *partenaire* to ask and answer questions about your schedules. Use a variety of question expressions including *où, à quelle heure,* and *quel cours*.

Modèle

Élève A: Quel cours as-tu à 11h00?

Élève B: J'ai le cours de géo à 11h00.

Activité 17

À quelle heure commencent et se terminent les cours?

📖 ✳ Étape 1: Observez et écrivez

Paul is a high school student in Plouzané, France. Look at his school schedule and say what time each class begins and ends. Alternate with a partner.

Modèle

Lundi, l'anglais commence à 10h10 et se termine à 11h05.

Mardi, l'espagnol commence à 14h55 et se termine à 15h50.

	lundi	mardi	mercredi	jeudi	vendredi
8h00-8h55	Histoire-géo (13)	Latin (26)	Arts plastiques	Histoire-géo (13)	SVT (15)
9h00-9h55	Français (7)	Maths (3)		Maths (3)	Espagnol (34)
10h10-11h05	Anglais (32)	EPS	Technologie (T2)	EPS	Technologie (T2)
11h10-12h05	SVT (15)				Maths (3)
Pause					
12h55-13h50					Latin (26)
13h55-14h50	Français (7)	Français (7)			Histoire-géo (13)
14h55-15h50	Espagnol (34)	Espagnol (34)	SVT (15)		Français (7)
16h05-17h00	Maths (3)	Anglais (32)			Anglais (32)

✎ ✦ **Étape 2: Écrivez**

Using the *Modèle* from *Étape 1*, write down four classes you have and what time each one begins and ends. Remember to use the 24-hour clock to express times in the afternoon. Record your answers in your Explorer course.

Cours 1:
Cours 2:
Cours 3:
Cours 4:

✦ Mon progrès communicatif

I can provide information about my school schedule using the 24-hour clock.

✎ ⊕ ✦ **Étape 3: Réfléchissez**

What similarities and differences do you notice between Paul's schedule and yours? Write your responses in the discussion forum in Explorer.

Modèle

Je suis comme Paul parce que j'étudie les maths.

Je suis différent(e) de Paul parce que je n'étudie pas le latin.

✦ Mon progrès interculturel

I can identify some simple similarities and differences between my schedule and one of a Francophone student.

J'avance 2

Nos emplois du temps

À CHAQUE CLASSE SON EMPLOI DU TEMPS

	6ᵉ	5ᵉ	4ᵉ	3ᵉ
Français	4h30	4h30	4h30	4h
Mathématiques	4h30	3h30	3h30	3h30
Histoire - géographie Enseignement moral et civique	3h	3h	3h	3h30
Langue vivante 1	4h	3h	3h	3h
Langue vivante 2	–	2h30	2h30	2h30
Sciences de la vie et de la Terre	4h	1h30	1h30	1h30
Sciences physiques		1h30	1h30	1h30
Technologie		1h30	1h30	1h30
Éducation physique et sportive	4h	3h	3h	3h
Arts plastiques	1h	1h	1h	1h
Éducation musicale	1h	1h	1h	1h

© Ministère de l'Éducation Nationale (2017), "À chaque classe son emploi du temps." Retrieved from http://www.education.gouv.fr/cid80/les-horaires-par-cycle-au-college.html.

📖 ⊙⊙ ✴ Étape 1: Lisez et identifiez

Read the infographic and identify two similarities and differences between the time expectations for each class in France and in your school. Note your findings in the *représentation schématique* in Explorer.

✴ **Mon progrès interculturel**

I can identify some simple similarities and differences between my schedule and one of a Francophone student.

📊 📊 📊

✏️ ✴️ Étape 2: Expliquez

Now write four sentences to express the time spent in your classes over the course of a week. Use start and end times to talk about four different classes.

💬 ✴️ Étape 3: Demandez

Your classmates may not feel the same way about class subjects as you do. So in order to learn which classes one of your classmates enjoys and why, you will ask him or her about four of your core classes. Record your findings in the chart in Explorer and remember that all of the materials for *J'avance 2* can be found in Explorer.

Mon progrès communicatif

I can provide information about my school schedule using the 24-hour clock.

Mon progrès communicatif

I can ask and answer questions about my class preferences.

Institut National Supérieur de Musique

Comment dit-on? 3

✦ Qu'est-ce qu'on fait à l'école?

Les activités des élèves

1. faire les devoirs

2. étudier dans un lycée bilingue

3. faire attention dans la salle de classe

4. déjeuner à la cantine

5. organiser le casier

6. utiliser un ordinateur à la médiathèque

7. discuter avec des amis dans la cour

8. travailler en équipe

Les activités des professeurs

9. enseigner le français au collège

10. aider un(e) élève

11. parler avec le/la principal(e)

Activité 18

  Ce que nous aimons faire à l'école

Listen to each statement as students describe activities they do at school, and write the number of the corresponding picture from *Comment dit-on? 3*.

A. _____ B. _____ C. _____ D. _____ E. _____ F. _____

Activité 19

 Dans mon école, il y a...

You are going to share a simple description with Hamid about the people and places at your school. How many people and places from the list below are at your school?

a. Combine an indefinite article from the left with the nouns on the right to describe your school.

b. Next, with a ***partenaire*** or in a small group compare your sentences and share them with the class.

Modèle

Dans mon école, il y a une cantine.

un	laboratoire(s)
une	casier(s)
des	salle(s) de classe
	gymnase(s)
	médiathèque(s)
	prof(s)
	cantine(s)
	élève(s)
	principal(e)

Mon progrès communicatif

I can identify common student activities and locations at school.

Détail grammatical

L'infinitif

In French, the most basic form of verbs (action words) is **l'infinitif** (*the infinitive*), the form that usually corresponds to the English verb preceded by "to." The French infinitive is just one word, and it always ends in either **-er**, **-ir**, or **-re**.

parler *to speak*

finir *to finish*

répondre *to respond/answer*

You have already learned how to use the infinitive with **j'aime** to express activities you like.

Est-ce que tu aimes **jouer** au foot?
Do you like to play soccer?

J'aime **étudier** au café.
I like to study at the cafe.

Activité 20

  ## Les endroits à l'école

You are giving a tour of your school to a new exchange student from Algeria. As you walk through the school, you describe activities that occur in each location. Match the following phrases about what students like to do at school with a list of school locations.

Modèle

Les élèves aiment déjeuner   à la cantine

1. Les élèves utilisent des ordinateurs	a. à l'école bilingue	
2. Les élèves aiment parler avec des autres élèves	b. dans le casier	
3. Je dois (*I must*) étudier le français et l'espagnol	c. à la médiathèque	
4. J'organise des livres et des fournitures scolaires	d. dans la salle de classe	
5. Les élèves aiment faire attention au professeur	e. dans la cour	

Activité 21

  Qui le dit?

In journalism class, you are proofreading an entry on the school blog about people at school. Working with a ***partenaire***, match the statements with the logical person.

Modèle

> Je mange avec mes amis
> à la cantine.

A	**B**	**C**	**D**
une élève	**un professeur**	**un principal**	**une agente de sécurité**

1. *J'aide mes élèves quand ils ont des difficultés.*

2. *J'étudie dans un lycée.*

3. *Je suis le chef (leader) de l'école.*

4. *Je fais attention en cours quand le professeur parle.*

5. *Je travaille pour la protection de l'école.*

6. *J'enseigne la biologie parce que j'aime les sciences.*

7. *J'étudie à la médiathèque avec mes amis.*

8. *Je parle des devoirs (homework) avec mes amis.*

9. *Je porte un uniforme pour travailler à l'école.*

On peut aussi dire

avoir une interro
to take a test

participer aux clubs
to rarticipate in clubs

travailler au bureau
to work in the office

Mon progrès communicatif

I can ask and answer questions about typical activities during the school day.

Mon progrès communicatif

I can identify some activities that students like to do at school.

Activité 22

Qu'est-ce que tu aimes faire?

💬 ⊕ Étape 1: Demandez et écrivez

You are preparing to participate in a video chat with Hamid's class in Algeria. To practice, ask at least five **élèves** in your class a question using the prompts below and record their answers in the **représentation schématique** (*graphic organizer*) in Explorer.

Modèle

Vous: Est-ce que tu aimes étudier le français?

Yasmine: Oui, j'aime étudier le français./Non, je n'aime pas étudier le français.

nom	réponse
Yasmine	oui
1.	
2.	

1. parler avec des amis pendant la récré?
2. déjeuner à la cantine?
3. jouer au basket au gymnase?
4. utiliser un ordinateur à la médiathèque?
5. étudier la biologie?
6. aider les autres élèves dans ton cours?
7. participer aux clubs?
8. faire les devoirs?

✏️ ⊕ Étape 2: Écrivez

In your class journal or in the Explorer discussion forum, summarize what you learned in your conversations with the **élèves** by writing at least five simple sentences that describe what each student likes or dislikes.

Modèle

Georges aime étudier le français.

Zoom culture

Pratique culturelle: La technologie à l'école

  Connexions

What technology is available to you at your school? How do you use technology in your classes? How does technology enhance and/or distract from learning?

Many schools in Algeria specify a cell phone policy in their *règlement intérieur* (*school handbook*). Policies vary, but range from all technological devices *(ordinateur, tablette et portable)* being banned from school grounds to usage only outside of buildings or covered areas. Most schools do have some *ordinateurs* and other devices available to students in the *médiathèque*. However, in order to use these devices students are required to have teacher authorization, a specific task, and an approved research plan.

In France, the *Ministre de l'Éducation nationale* has a specific plan that was announced by former president François Hollande in 2015 to bring schools into the digital age. This plan includes a database of lessons for teachers and more technology available to students. According to this plan, all French students in grade 6 and 7 should have an individual device in 2018. There is even a hashtag: *#écolenumérique*.

  Réflexion

How does technology influence perspectives at your school and at schools in Francophone countries? What impact do these perspectives of technology have on students? On teachers? On the community?

Réflexion interculturelle

  How do cultural values impact perspectives of technology in the classroom? How might future technology change the way we interact with people in our community and people in other countries? Answer the questions in the discussion forum in Explorer.

 Mon progrès interculturel

I can identify practices and related perspectives regarding the use of technology in schools in Francophone countries.

Activité 23

🎧 ✦ **Où est-ce qu'on le fait?**

You are attending a new school and you need to know where to go for various activities during the school day. Listen to the statements and match them with a logical location. Some activities might be logical in multiple locations.

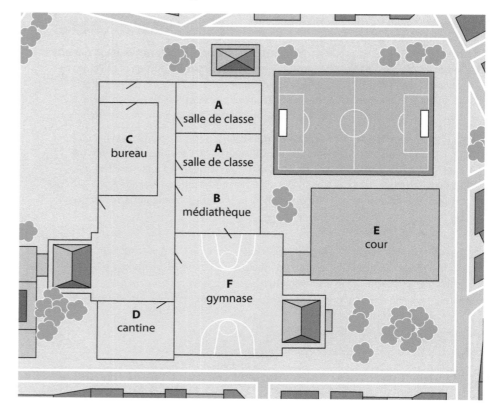

1. _____   2. _____   3. _____   4. _____

5. _____   6. _____   7. _____   8. _____

Mon progrès communicatif

I can identify common student activities and locations at school.

Oran, Algérie

Découvrons 3

Expressing Daily School Activities

Océane and Félix have a conversation about their daily activities that are centered around their day at school.

Découvertes

During this conversation, notice the words in bold that specify actions (verbs). Look carefully at the endings and try to figure out from the context who is doing each action. What do you observe about the different forms? Do you notice any patterns? How many different endings do you notice? Discuss your observations with your *partenaires* and with your teacher. View the *Découvrons 3* resources in Explorer and the *Synthèse de grammaire* at the end of the unit.

Activité 24

📖 **Moi aussi!**

Read the following sentences from the conversation between Océane and Félix and choose a response that is true for you.

1. «*Mon prof d'anglais enseigne la culture anglaise.*»

    a. Oui, mon prof d'anglais enseigne aussi la culture anglaise.

    b. Non, mon prof d'anglais enseigne la culture et la littérature américaine.

2. «*Nous participons beaucoup en cours.*»

    a. Oui, nous participons beaucoup en cours.

    b. Non, nous ne participons pas beaucoup en cours.

3. «*Je déjeune à midi.*»

    a. Oui, je déjeune à midi.

    b. Non, je ne déjeune pas à midi.

4. «*Tu aimes la cuisine à l'école?*»

    a. Oui, j'aime la cuisine à l'école.

    b. Non, je préfère la cuisine au restaurant.

5. «*Ils (mes amis) écoutent de la musique américaine.*»

    a. Mes amis écoutent aussi de la musique américaine.

    b. Mes amis écoutent de la musique française.

6. «*Je rentre chez moi après l'école.*»

    a. Oui, je rentre chez moi après l'école.

    b. Non, je rentre chez moi après le sport et les activités.

7. «*Je regarde la télévision.*»

    a. Oui, je regarde la télévision.

    b. Non, j'aime lire un bon livre.

8. «*Je commence mes devoirs à 17h.*»

    a. Oui, je commence mes devoirs à 17h.

    b. Moi, je commence mes devoirs après le dîner.

Rappel

Remember to incorporate verbs like **danser, chanter, manger, dessiner, regarder** from previous units as you complete tasks.

Détail grammatical

Les pronoms sujets et les verbes en -er

You have seen numerous instances of **je** and **tu** with conjugated verbs and the endings of **-e** and **-es**. Take note of the other pronouns and the verb endings.

je (I) parl**e**	**nous** (we) parl**ons**
tu (you) parl**es**	**vous** (you) parl**ez**
il/elle (he/she/it) parl**e**	**ils/elles** (they) parl**ent**

Note: This chart shows the present tense of the French verb **parler**. **Je parle** can have several meanings in English – I speak, I am speaking, and I do speak.

Activité 25

Un jour typique

  Étape 1: Lisez et répondez

You have received an email from Hamid asking you questions about your typical day at school. Read the message and answer the questions, following the **Modèle**, to show your understanding of his typical day at school.

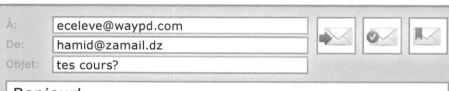

À: eceleve@waypd.com
De: hamid@zamail.dz
Objet: tes cours?

Bonjour!

Ça va? Tu commences les cours quand? Mon cours de biologie commence à 8h30. Dimanche matin, j'ai aussi l'anglais et l'arabe. J'aide mon ami, Karim, en arabe. Tu étudies quelles langues? Je déjeune à la cantine à 12h30. Où déjeunes-tu? J'aime le cours de maths parce qu'il est intéressant. Quels cours aimes-tu? Je termine les cours à 16h30. À quelle heure termines-tu les cours? Après, je joue du piano et j'étudie à la maison. Je ne fais pas de sport mais je fais mes devoirs.

À plus,

Hamid

Modèle

Hamid étudie l'histoire le dimanche?

Non, il n'étudie pas l'histoire le dimanche.

1. Est-ce que Hamid joue au foot?
2. À quelle heure est-ce qu'il commence les cours le dimanche?
3. Où est-ce qu'il étudie?
4. Est-ce qu'il aide ses amis en cours?
5. Quelles langues est-ce qu'il étudie?
6. Où est-ce qu'il déjeune? À quelle heure?

✦ Étape 2: Écrivez

Respond to Hamid's email to tell him about your typical school day. Answer the questions from his email and add any other important or interesting information about your school day. Use the present tense *je* form of verbs that end in *-er* that you have learned and other expressions from this unit.

> Cher Hamid,
>
> Ça va bien. Et toi? Mon cours de...

⓪ ◉ ✦ Étape 3: Comparez

Compare your typical school day to that of Hamid. With a *partenaire* take turns sharing similarities and differences.

Modèle

Je suis comme Hamid parce que…

Je ne suis pas comme Hamid parce que…

Activité 26

📖 ✦ Qui le fait?

On a typical day at school, the following activities are taking place. Use a subject pronoun to express who is doing each action by following the model. Then number the statements in chronological order from morning to evening.

I̶l̶; elle; nous; vous; ils; la prof, elle

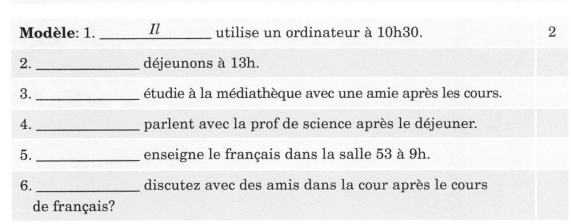

Modèle: 1. _____*Il*_____ utilise un ordinateur à 10h30.   2

2. _____ déjeunons à 13h.

3. _____ étudie à la médiathèque avec une amie après les cours.

4. _____ parlent avec la prof de science après le déjeuner.

5. _____ enseigne le français dans la salle 53 à 9h.

6. _____ discutez avec des amis dans la cour après le cours de français?

Activité 27

Un blog: Bienvenue à notre école

✏️ 🧭 Étape 1: Écrivez

Your school will be hosting a student exchange group from Algeria. Your class has created a blog to establish communication between your school and the school in Algeria. Your first task is to write a blog post to describe what people in your school do and where.

Write six logical sentences using one element from each column in the chart below. Be sure that the subject in column 1 matches the verb form in column 2 and then pick the appropriate location from column 3.

1	2	3
Nous	écoutes de la musique	dans le gymnase.
Les élèves	déjeune avec des amis	dans la salle de classe de madame Smith.
Je (J')	jouons au basket	à la médiathèque.
Vous	étudient l'anglais	dans la cantine.
Tu (Océane)	utilisez un ordinateur	dans la salle de sciences.
Il (le prof)	enseigne la biologie	dans la cour.

✏️ 🧭 Étape 2: Préparez

You are going to make a video blog entry describing a typical day at school. To prepare for your blog, write some notes about your classes, times, and extracurricular activities.

a. Use the verbs listed below and look up others that you may need.

b. In addition to describing what you normally do, you can also mention what classmates and teachers do as well.

c. Pay special attention to the verb endings that accompany the pronouns that indicate who does each action.

aider, danser, chanter, étudier, parler, participer, discuter, travailler, déjeuner, jouer, enseigner, regarder, organiser

🎤 ⊕ Étape 3: Filmez

Record your video blog in Explorer. Don't forget to practice before you film so that you are comfortable.

Activité 28

Activité 28

Une interview pour le blog

💬 Étape 1: Préparez

Your teacher has asked you to add more content to your class blog for the students in Algeria by interviewing a classmate and asking questions about his or her typical school day.

Prepare your interview questions with a *partenaire* or small group by writing at least six questions for a classmate. Be sure to include yes/no questions (conjugated verb + *tu*) and information questions (question words like *où, pourquoi, à quelle heure,* etc.+ *tu* + conjugated verb).

Modèle

Utilises-tu un ordinateur dans la médiathèque?

À quelle heure as-tu le cours d'histoire?

💬 ⊕ Étape 2: Demandez et répondez

Ask and answer your questions from *Étape 1* with a different *partenaire*. Then your *partenaire* will ask you six questions about your school day. Record your conversation live in Explorer.

☑ 👥 ⊕ Étape 3: Résumez

Summarize what you learned about your classmate and his or her typical school day by writing three summary sentences to be shared in the class blog with the students in Algeria.

Modèle

Il/Elle étudie les maths et les sciences.

Mon progrès communicatif

I can identify common student activities and locations at school.

J'avance 3

Mes activités à l'école

Étape 1: Regardez

You will hear Océane describe the things that she does at school from her video post that appears on her blog, an online personal journal where she shares her thoughts and experiences. Place a check (✔) next to the phrases in the chart that are true according to the video.

Étape 2: Lisez et écrivez

You received an email from Océane asking you about your school experience. Read her email and then write a response in Explorer. and remember that all of the materials for ***J'avance 3*** can be found in Explorer.

 Mon progrès communicatif

I can respond to an email from a Francophone student about typical activities during the school day.

Constantine, Algérie

Synthèse de grammaire

1. Expressing Number and Gender: *les articles indéfinis*

In French, the indefinite article (similar to *a/an* or *some* in English) has three basic forms, **un**, **une**, and **des**, depending on the gender (masculine or feminine) and number (singular or plural) of the noun.

un crayon (masc. sing.)	a pencil	**des** crayons (masc. pl.)	(some) pencils
une calculatrice (fem. sing.)	a calculator	**des** calculatrices (fem. pl.)	(some) calculators

After a negative expression, the indefinite article will become **de/d'**.

Il y a **un** ordinateur dans mon sac à dos.
Il n'y a pas **d'**ordinateurs dans mon sac à dos.

J'ai **des** crayons dans ma trousse.
Je n'ai pas **de** crayons dans ma trousse.

Les articles définis et la possession avec de

The definite article (similar to *the* in English) has three basic forms, **le**, **la**, and **les**, depending on the gender and number of the noun.

le crayon	the pencil	**les** crayons	the pencils
la calculatrice	the calculator	**les** calculatrices	the calculators

The definite article sometimes is not translated into English when it refers to something in general.

J'aime **la** biologie. *I like biology.*
Nous aimons **les** chansons françaises. *We like French songs.*

Definite articles can be used with the preposition **de** to show possession. The formula for showing possession is to use a *definite article + noun + **de/d'** + name*.

La calculatrice de Paul est moderne. *Paul's calculator is modern.*

2. Telling Time: *l'heure*

In French, one can ask about the time in several ways:

Quelle heure est-il? or **Il est quelle heure?**	*What time is it?*
Tu as l'heure? or **Est-ce que tu as l'heure?**	*Do you have the time?*

The *il* is an impersonal "it," as in <u>It</u> is 10:00.

Il est 10h11. (Il est dix heures onze.)	*It is ten eleven AM.*
Il est 13h21. (Il est treize heures vingt et une.)	*It is one twenty-one PM.*
Il est 23h58. (Il est vingt-trois heures cinquante-huit.)	*It is eleven fifty-eight PM.*

3. Expressing Daily School Activities: *les verbes en -er*

The basic form of the verb (action word) in French is the infinitive, which can end in *-er, -ir,* and *-re* (e.g., *parler, finir, répondre*).

To talk about customary actions and general facts, we use a form of the verb called the present tense. For infinitives that end in *-er*, look at the endings for each of our subject pronouns for the of the verb *chanter*:

je chante	nous chantons
tu chantes	vous chantez
il/elle/on chante	ils/elles chantent

Je **parle** anglais avec ma famille.	*I speak English with my family.*
Nous n'**étudions** pas le latin.	*We do not study Latin.*

Note that in these two sentences, there is not a separate French word that corresponds to the English *do* or *is*.

On is a more generic pronoun used to refer to people in general, such as in the sentence, "One speaks French in France"/***On parle français en France.***

Vocabulaire

Comment dit-on? 1: I can say what I have and need for school.

Les fournitures scolaires	*School supplies*
l'agenda (m.) scolaire	school planner
le cahier	notebook
la calculatrice	calculator
les ciseaux (m.pl.)	scissors
le classeur	binder
le crayon	pencil
le dictionnaire	dictionary
la feuille de papier	sheet of paper
le livre	book
l'ordinateur (m.)	computer
le portable	cell phone
le sac à dos	backpack
le stylo	pen
la tablette	tablet
la trousse	pencil case

Les numéros de 30 à 69	*The numbers from 30 to 69*
trente	thirty
quarante	forty
quarante-quatre	forty-four
cinquante	fifty
cinquante-sept	fifty-seven
soixante	sixty
soixante-neuf	sixty-nine

Comment dit-on? 2: I can exchange information about classes and schedules and talk about my school.

Expressions utiles

parce que/qu'	because
pendant la semaine	during the week
pendant le week-end	during the weekend

L'heure / *Time*

À quelle heure?	At what time?
Quelle heure est-il?	What time is it?
Le cours commence à...	The class begins at...
Le cours se termine à...	The class ends at...

Stratégies: Cognates

l'algèbre (f.)	algebra
l'arabe (m.)	Arabic
les arts (m. pl.) visuels	visual arts
la biologie	biology
la chorale	chorus
le latin	Latin
l'orchestre (m.)	orchestra
la psychologie	psychology
les sciences (f.pl.) sociales	social studies
le sport [EPS = l'éducation (f.) physique et sportive]	physical education

Les matières	School subjects
l'anglais (m.)	English
le cours	class, course
le déjeuner	lunch
l'éducation (f.) physique et sportive (EPS)	physical education
l'espagnol (m.)	Spanish
le français	French
la physique	physics
la géographie	geography
l'histoire (f.)	history
l'informatique (f.)	technology
les langues (f.pl.) vivantes	modern languages
la littérature	literature
les mathématiques (f.pl.) (les maths)	math
la musique	music
la récréation (la récré)	recess/break
les sciences (f. pl.) de la vie et de la terre (SVT)	life and earth science
les sciences (f. pl.) sociales	social studies
difficile	difficult
facile	easy
fascinant/fascinante	fascinating

Comment dit-on? 3: I can talk about people, places, and activities at school.

Les activités	Activities
aider	to help
déjeuner	to eat lunch
discuter	to discuss
enseigner	to teach
étudier	to study
faire attention	to pay attention
organiser	to organize
parler	to speak
travailler en équipe	to work in teams
utiliser	to use

Les lieux et des personnes de l'école	People and places at school
le/la prof	teacher
le/la principal(e)	principal
la cantine	cafeteria
le casier	locker
le collège	middle school
la cour	courtyard
l'école (f.)	school
le gymnase	gymnasium
le lycée	high school
la médiathèque	library, media center
la salle de classe	classroom

Une école au Burkina Faso

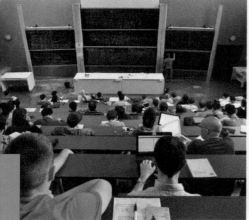

Une école à Paris, en France

J'y arrive

Questions essentielles

- How is student life at my school similar to and/or different from student life in a Francophone country?

- How do courses and schedules reflect the educational values of a community?

- What places, people, and activities define student life?

Un échange virtuel

Your teacher has set up an e-pal exchange with Hamid's class in Algeria. You are paired with one of his classmates, Sofia. Your goal is to gather information about her school building, class schedule, and activities in order to learn more about schools in Algeria and compare what you learn to your own school experience. Before you begin, refer to the *J'y arrive* rubric in Explorer to familiarize yourself with the evaluation criteria.

Interpretive Assessment

Les cours de Sofia

Sofia has shared her class schedule with you so that you can compare her schedule and her school with yours.

Étape 1: Associez

Complete the ***représentation schématique*** *(graphic organizer)* in Explorer with the classes and possible activities that take place in each location. Be sure to include at least one class and one activity for each location.

Étape 2: Comparez

Using the information from Sofia's schedule and ***Étape 1***, write one similarity and one difference between class schedules in Algeria and in your community.

Des élèves en Algérie

Interpersonal Assessment

Un tchat avec Sofia

Sofia wants to learn more about your school and schedule. You are able to schedule a time to chat online to exchange information about your school preferences. Respond to her questions and ask her any appropriate questions in the chat in Explorer.

Presentational Assessment

Un jour à l'école

Sofia wants to know more about your school, classes, and activities. Create either a video visit or a visual presentation about your school day to share with her. Follow the directions in Explorer to create and share your video.

UNITÉ 3
La vie en famille

Objectifs de l'unité

Exchange information about family and home life.

Interpret print texts, infographics, charts, graphs, audios, and videos about family life and activities.

Present a collection of images to share information about a home, a family and/or friends.

Explore family life in Francophone cultures.

⊕ Questions essentielles

Who are the members of a family?

Which attributes and interests do family members share?

Which places and activities bring families together in our culture and in Francophone cultures?

Family and traditions make us unique and define who we are. Often when you meet new people, you want to talk about those closest to you and the things you do together. In this unit, you will meet Jeanne from southwest France, who will introduce you to her family through her video blog. You will also hear from other bloggers who will introduce you to their families.

Rencontre interculturelle
Le sud-ouest de la France

La Nouvelle-Aquitaine est bordée par l'Océan Atlantique (à l'ouest) et l'Espagne (au sud). Il y a aussi des montagnes dans la région, les Pyrénées. Pau, la ville d'origine de Jeanne, est dans la partie nord des Pyrénées. Bordeaux est la plus grande ville de la région.

Nom: Jeanne

Langues parlées: français, espagnol, anglais

Origine: Pau, France

La Nouvelle-Aquitaine, une région dans le sud de la France

Le sud-ouest de l'Europe

Biarritz, Nouvelle-Aquitaine, France

Jeanne aime les mangas, un genre de bande dessinée ou de dessin animé.

La famille de Jeanne: François, Lysia, Jeanne et Emmanuel

Poitiers, Nouvelle-Aquitaine, France

Je m'appelle Jeanne.

J'adore la musique et j'écoute particulièrement le rock.

Je joue du hautbois (oboe).

J'aime lire les mangas.

Tous les membres de la famille de Jeanne sont originaires de la Nouvelle-Aquitaine, dans le sud-ouest de la France. Elle habite avec sa maman, son papa et son frère, François. Elle a un chien, Loki.

Activité 1

Bonjour, Jeanne!

📖 Étape 1: Préparez

Look at the photo of Jeanne and what is in her speech bubbles. Which types of information do you think she has included in her video blog? Which interests does she mention?

📹 🖊 🧭 Étape 2: Écoutez et écrivez

Watch Jeanne's video blog and note some information about her family and interests in the *diagramme de Venn* in Explorer. Do not try to write complete sentences: Use an image, word or short phrase to remind yourself of what you heard. If you have something in common with Jeanne, make sure to list it in the center of the *diagramme de Venn*.

✐ ✵ Étape 3: Écrivez

Now take some time to add images, words or short phrases to the circle in the *diagramme de Venn* labeled *moi* that describe you, your family or those important to you, and your interests.

◍ ◉ ✵ Étape 4: Comparez et discutez

How is Jeanne similar to you and how is she different from you? Share some of your comparisons with a classmate and use your *diagramme de Venn* to help you.

Modèle
....

Je suis comme Jeanne. J'aime la musique aussi.

Réflexion interculturelle

◍ ✵ Where are you from? Which activities do you like to do where you live? How is Jeanne similar to and/or different from you? Answer the questions in the discussion forum in Explorer.

> ✵ **Mon progrès interculturel**
>
> I can identify some similarities and differences between a Francophone teen and myself related to preferences and place of origin.

Saint-Martin-de-Ré, Nouvelle-Aquitaine, France

Communiquons
Comment dit-on? 1
✦ C'est ma famille

La famille DURAND

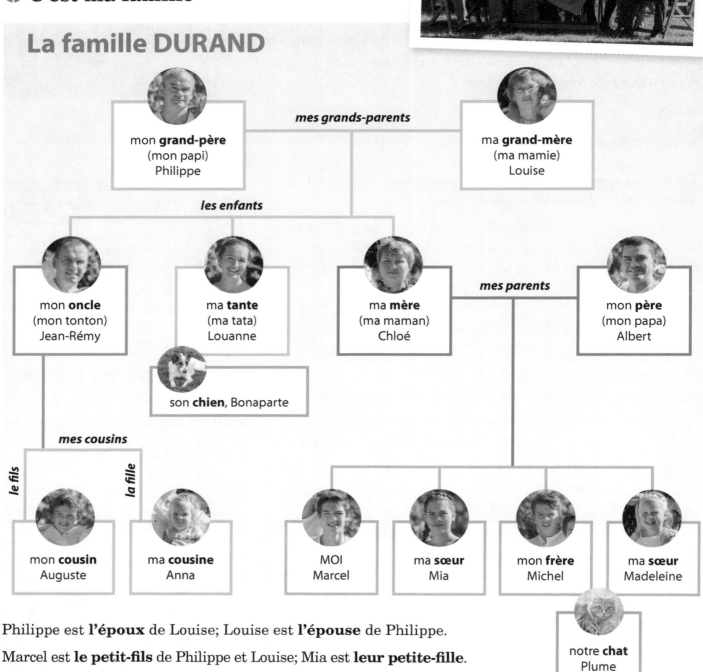

Philippe est **l'époux** de Louise; Louise est **l'épouse** de Philippe.

Marcel est **le petit-fils** de Philippe et Louise; Mia est **leur petite-fille**.

Auguste est **le neveu** d'Albert et Chloé; Anna est **leur nièce**.

Nous sommes sept. **J'ai** une mère et un père. J'ai aussi un frère, deux sœurs et un chat.

Activité 2

  C'est qui?

Decide if each sentence about Marcel's family is **vraie** (*true*) or **fausse** (*false*) based on the information in the family tree. Rewrite the false sentences to make them **vraies**.

1. Albert est le père de Mia.

2. Louanne est la sœur de Chloé.

3. Auguste est le frère de Madeleine.

4. Marcel est le fils de Jean-Rémy.

5. Louanne est la tante de Madeleine.

6. Philippe est l'oncle d'Anna.

7. Louise a six petits-enfants.

8. Michel est le petit-fils de Louise et Albert.

Activité 3

La famille de mon père

Marcel has written you a message to tell you about other members of his family, specifically his paternal lineage.

À:	eceleve@waypd.com
De:	marceld@wmel.fr
Objet:	ma famille

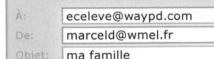

Salut!

Dans ma famille, nous sommes sept avec notre chat Plume. J'ai un petit frère et deux sœurs. Mon frère, Michel, aime jouer du piano comme mon oncle, Luc. Luc est le frère cadet de mon père et il a une épouse qui s'appelle Émilie. Oncle Luc est très amusant mais avec le piano, il est très sérieux. Luc et Émilie n'ont pas d'enfants, mais ils ont un chien dynamique et un gros lapin 🐰. Tu as des animaux?

J'ai aussi une grand-mère, la mère de mon père, Albert. Elle s'appelle Alice et elle a 78 ans. Antoine est l'époux de ma grand-mère. C'est le beau-père d'Albert et Luc. Le père d'Albert et de Luc est mort en 1975. Ma grand-mère et Antoine habitent à Bordeaux et ils aiment les vacances près de l'océan Atlantique, surtout avec nous. Nous aimons nager et passer du temps à la plage avec toute la famille. Qu'est-ce que tu aimes faire avec ta famille?

Et toi? Décris-moi un peu ta famille ou les personnes que tu aimes.

Marcel

On peut aussi dire

Families are made up of many different members. In French, we use different prefixes to indicate different family relationships. These prefixes can be added to different family member terms as needed.

l'arrière-grand-mère
great-grandmother

l'arrière-grand-père
great-grandfather

le beau-père
step-father, father-in-law

la belle-mère
step-mother, mother-in-law

le demi-frère
half-brother

la demi-sœur
half-sister

aîné(e)
oldest

le bébé
baby

cadet(te)
youngest

la femme
wife

le mari
husband

Étape 1: Complétez

To make sure you understand who the family members are, complete the sentences with the appropriate name(s) that make(s) the sentence *vraie*.

1. _____ est le beau-père d'Albert et de Luc.

2. _____ et _____ ont un chien dynamique.

3. La grand-mère de Mia s'appelle _____.

4. _____ et _____ jouent du piano.

5. Le chat de Marcel s'appelle _____.

Étape 2: Écrivez

Respond to Marcel's message by describing at least three people or animals who play an important role in your life. Be sure to include their names, relationship to you, and something interesting about them.

Activité 4

Les familles de Kate et de Jeanne

Étape 1: Regardez

Read the list of family words below, then watch the video of Kate, our video blogger from Togo, in which she tells us about her family. Put a checkmark (✔) next to the vocabulary words you hear in Kate's description.

1. ____ famille

2. ____ mère

3. ____ tante

4. ____ chat

5. ____ chien

6. ____ fille

7. ____ frère

8. ____ père

9. ____ enfant

10. ____ sœur

▶️ ✳️ Étape 2: Regardez

Now watch the video of Jeanne describing her family and mark the words you hear in the ***représentation schématique*** provided in your Explorer course.

🎤 ✳️ Étape 3: Parlez

Introduce your own family, an imaginary family or a famous one to present to Jeanne via video chat. Mention several members of the family and how you may be related to each person.

> ✳️ **Mon progrès communicatif**
>
> I can identify family members when I hear someone talk about his or her family.
>
> 📶 📶 📶

Activité 5

💬 L'arbre généalogique

Work with a ***partenaire*** to describe a real or imagined family tree. One ***partenaire*** starts by describing a family with at least three members while the other ***partenaire*** draws the accompanying family tree. The ***partenaire*** drawing the family tree should ask clarifying questions to get more information. Then switch roles and do it again.

Modèle

Élève A: J'ai un père et un frère.

Élève B: Comment s'appelle ton père?

Élève A: Mon père s'appelle David.

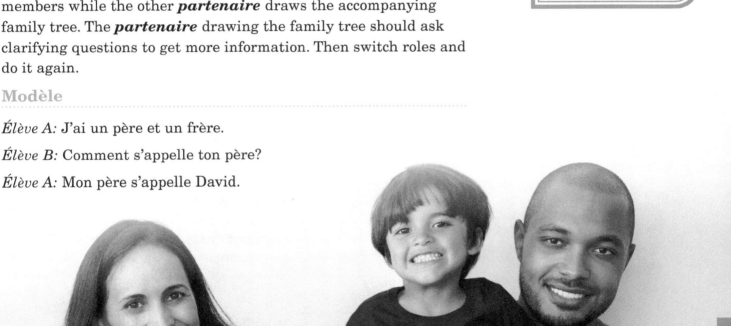

⊕ **Mon progrès communicatif**

I can identify the actions of family members in a *comptine*, a French nursery rhyme.

Activité 6

  ⊕ *Toute la famille*

Toute la famille is a French *comptine*, similar to a nursery rhyme, that tells the tale of a family as they awaken for a new day. Match the family members with actions that are associated with them in the *comptine*.

1. Le père
2. La mère
3. La grand-mère
4. Les enfants
5. Le grand-père

a. est à pied
b. attrapent le chat
c. met de la musique
d. démarre la voiture
e. fait des confitures
f. fait sa gymnastique

¹ la famille se réveille

² les volets

³ il fait sa gymnastique

⁴ elle met de la musique

⁵ ils attrapent les chats

⁶ il démarre la voiture

⁷ la confiture

⁸ il est parti à pied

Toute la famille
par Bernard François et Pierre Lozère

Toute la famille se réveille¹,
ouvrez, ouvrez les volets²
toute la famille se réveille
la journée peut commencer.

Papa fait sa gymnastique³
un, deux, trois, quatre,
Maman met de la musique⁴
les enfants attrapent le chat!⁵

Toute la famille se réveille,
ouvrez ouvrez les volets
toute la famille se réveille
la journée peut commencer.

Papa démarre la voiture⁶
Un, deux, trois quatre,
Grand-mère fait des confitures⁷
Les enfants attrapent le chat!

Toute la famille se réveille,
ouvrez, ouvrez les volets
toute la famille se réveille
la journée peut commencer.

Grand-père est parti à pied⁸
Un, deux, trois, quatre,
La confiture est brûlée
Les enfants attrapent le chat!⁵

Toute la famille se réveille,
ouvrez, ouvrez les volets
toute la famille se réveille
la journée peut commencer.

Activité 7

Combien de personnes?

📖 🌐 Étape 1: Lisez

Read the descriptions of different families from an online survey about Francophone families. Note how many people and animals make up each family.

ma famille et nos chats

Moi, j'ai une sœur, Estelle, et deux chats. J'adore mes chats. J'habite aussi avec ma mère qui s'appelle Vivienne. J'adore ma famille.

une grande famille

J'ai une grande famille. Mon frère, Armand, et moi, nous habitons avec mes grands-parents et mon oncle, Jacques. Jacques a une épouse et trois enfants. Mes cousins s'appellent Camille, Léo et Victor.

la famille Dubois

J'habite avec mon père, Arthur, et son épouse, ma belle-mère. J'ai aussi un beau-frère qui habite avec nous. Nous avons un chien qui s'appelle Bisou.

🗒 🌐 Étape 2: Écrivez

You decide to practice your French by answering the survey questions as well. Write a short description like the examples in *Étape 1*. Don't forget to add a title and include at least three people or animals whom you consider part of your family.

Détail linguistique

Les petits noms familiaux

The names that people use to refer to family members may vary between families in Francophone countries and regions. Which family members do you think these nicknames represent?

mémé

bonne-maman

bon-papa

pépé

tatie

nanou

mimi

papichou

Activité 8

Les familles belges et françaises

📖 📝 ✤ **Étape 1: Préparez**

Look at the two graphs and note what you see, what you think, and
write some questions in the *organisateur en forme d'Y* in Explorer.

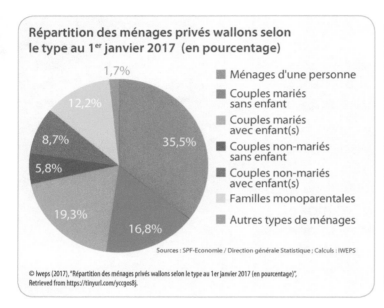

**Répartition des ménages privés wallons selon
le type au 1er janvier 2017 (en pourcentage)**

- 1,7%
- 12,2%
- 8,7%
- 5,8%
- 19,3%
- 16,8%
- 35,5%

- ■ Ménages d'une personne
- ■ Couples mariés sans enfant
- ■ Couples mariés avec enfant(s)
- ■ Couples non-mariés sans enfant
- ■ Couples non-mariés avec enfant(s)
- ■ Familles monoparentales
- ■ Autres types de ménages

Sources : SPF-Economie / Direction générale Statistique ; Calculs : IWEPS

© Iweps (2017), "Répartition des ménages privés wallons selon le type au 1er janvier 2017 (en pourcentage)",
Retrieved from https://tinyurl.com/yccgos8j.

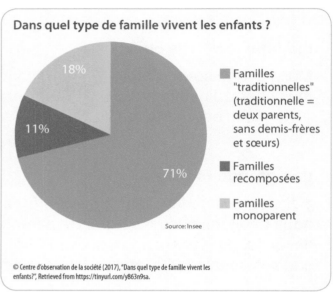

Dans quel type de famille vivent les enfants ?

- 18%
- 11%
- 71%

- ■ Familles "traditionnelles" (traditionnelle = deux parents, sans demis-frères et sœurs)
- ■ Familles recomposées
- ■ Familles monoparent

Source: Insee

© Centre d'observation de la société (2017), "Dans quel type de famille vivent les
enfants?", Retrieved from https://tinyurl.com/y863n9sa.

🌐 ◎ ✤ **Étape 2: Comparez et discutez**

Compare your findings from Belgium and France with
this data from the United States and add to your *organisateur en
forme d'Y*. Then discuss what you learned about families in
all three countries with a *partenaire* or small group.

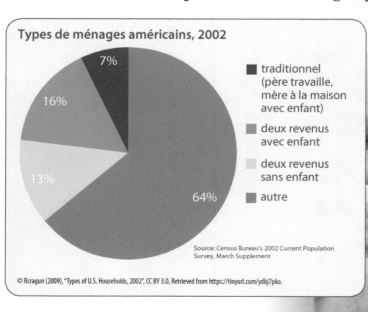

Types de ménages américains, 2002

- 7%
- 16%
- 13%
- 64%

- ■ traditionnel (père travaille, mère à la maison avec enfant)
- ■ deux revenus avec enfant
- ■ deux revenus sans enfant
- ■ autre

Source: Census Bureau's 2002 Current Population
Survey, March Supplement

© Rcragun (2009), "Types of U.S. Households, 2002", CC BY 3.0, Retrieved from https://tinyurl.com/ydbj7pko.

Réflexion interculturelle

 What are the different definitions of a family? What information from the different countries surprises you? Answer the questions in the discussion forum in Explorer.

Zoom culture

Pratique culturelle: Les animaux de compagnie

Un chien au café

Jeanne et son chien, Loki

  **Connexion**

How does the importance of household pets reflect the perspectives of a region or country?

France ranks in the top nine countries in the world for cat, dog, bird, and fish populations. There are 17 dogs for every 100 people in France. It is not uncommon for pets to be considered and treated as family members. Grooming facilities and pet bakeries are popular, and there are pet cemeteries in some communities. Pets may be seen accompanying their owners on outings around town, even in many restaurants and shops. In Quebec, pet friendly excursions are offered to well-behaved, leashed dogs. In Belgium, one in four families owns a cat and one in five a dog.

Réflexion

Research the facts about pet ownership in other Francophone countries or regions. How common is it for a family to have a pet? Do pets tend to live indoors or outdoors and do they participate in family outings or activities? What does the status of pets reveal about cultural perspectives in any given community? Provide your answers in the discussion forum in Explorer.

Découvrons 1

Indicating Family Relationships

Voici Jean-Rémy, **mon** oncle. Il a deux enfants. **Sa** fille s'appelle Anna et **son** fils s'appelle Auguste. **Ses** enfants sont **mes** cousins.

Louanne est **ma** tante et la sœur de Jean-Rémy. Elle a un chien. Bonaparte est **son** chien.

Voici Auguste, **mon** cousin. J'ai deux cousins, **mon** cousin Auguste et **ma** cousine Anna.

C'est **ma** sœur, Mia.

C'est **mon** frère, Michel.

Chloé est **notre** mère. Chloé et Albert sont **nos** parents.

C'est Anna, **ma** cousine. Nous avons les mêmes (same) grands-parents. Philippe et Louise sont **nos** grands-parents. Jean-Rémy est **leur** fils.

Louise est **ma** grand-mère et Philippe est **mon** grand-père. Ils ont trois enfants. Chloé, Louanne et Jean-Rémy sont **leurs** enfants.

C'est moi, Marcel!

Voici **ma** sœur, Madeleine.

C'est **notre** père, Albert.

Notre chat, Plume, est adorable.

Bonaparte est le chien de **ma** tante Louanne.

Découvertes

📖 📹 🧭 Read Marcel's descriptions of his family members, noticing the words in bold. What do you observe about the different forms? When does he use **mon** as opposed to **ma** or **mes**? When are **son**, **sa**, and **ses** used? How about **notre** and **nos**? What family relationships do these words indicate? Discuss with your classmates and teachers, view the **Découvrons 1** resources for this unit in your Explorer course, and check the **Synthèse de grammaire** at the end of this section to find out.

Activité 9

Qui sont-ils?

 Étape 1: Lisez

Combine a phrase from the left column with a phrase in the right column to create a sentence that Marcel could use to describe his family.

1. Louanne est
2. Mia et Madeleine sont
3. Louise est
4. Anna et Auguste sont
5. Philippe et Louise sont
6. Albert est

a. mon frère
b. ma grand-mère
c. notre tante
d. mes cousines
e. mes sœurs
f. ma cousine
g. mes cousins
h. nos grands-parents
i. mon père

 Étape 2: Écrivez

Identify members of a famous family using sentences like the ones in *Étape 1* or introduce your own family members as Marcel has done in *Découvrons 1*. If you choose to use a famous family, take the identity of one of the members of the family as if it's your own. Two family trees of famous families are available to you in Explorer. Use vocabulary from *Comment dit-on? 1, On peut aussi dire, Découvrons 1,* or look up the words you need.

Modèle

Ma mère est Cecilia.

Yannick est mon père.

Détail grammatical

Le verbe **avoir**

The verb **avoir**, one of the most commonly used verbs in French, allows people to say what they have.

j'ai	*I have*
tu as	*you have (informal, one person)*
il/elle a	*he/she has*
nous avons	*we have*
vous avez	*you have (formal or more than one person)*
ils/elles ont	*they have*

Note that to talk about what one does not have, **ne** and **pas** surround the verb. Since all the forms of **avoir** begin with a vowel, **ne** will become **n'** such as in:

je **n'**ai pas
nous **n'**avons pas
elles **n'**ont pas

Activité 10

Les relations familiales

Marcel is a new student at your school and he will shadow you for a day to help him become acquainted with the school routines and meet people. You can see from Marcel's family photo that he has siblings and also extended family, but you want to remind yourself of their names so you will be able to talk about his family to your friends.

✒️ ✥ Étape 1: Notez

Write a few questions that you'd like to ask Marcel about his family.

Modèle

Qui sont tes sœurs?

Comment s'appelle ta cousine?

💬 ✥ Étape 2: Demandez et répondez

How would Marcel answer your questions? Take turns with a *partenaire* being the one who asks questions.

Modèle

Élève A: Qui sont tes sœurs?

Élève B: Mia et Madeleine sont mes sœurs.

Élève B: Anna est ta cousine?

Élève A: Oui, Anna est ma cousine.

🎤 ✥ Étape 3: Parlez

Use the same information to introduce a few members of Marcel's family to a friend in your class.

Modèle

Mia et Madeleine sont ses sœurs.

Leur cousine s'appelle Anna.

✦ Mon progrès communicatif

I can ask and answer questions about family members in a photo.

Activité 11

  Et ta famille?

To learn more about Francophone families around the world, you decide to set up a *tchat* with Hamid. Read his messages and respond appropriately.

20:00

Hamid:

Salut! Ça va?

toi:

...

Ça va très bien, merci. J'ai un petit frère, il s'appelle Nassim. Tu as un frère ou une sœur?

...

Oui, ma grand-mère paternelle habite avec nous. C'est la mère de mon père. Elle s'appelle Myriam. Tu as des grands-parents? Ils habitent avec toi?

...

Oui, j'ai un chat. Je l'aime beaucoup. Tu as un animal?

...

Super! C'est intéressant de voir d'autres familles. Merci pour le tchat. À la prochaine.

...

Prononciation

▶️ 🧭 Liaison

In French, you will often see a consonant at the end of words that is generally silent.

vous mangez   les chiens   mes tantes

However, if the following word starts with a vowel or silent **h**, the final consonant is pronounced and it sounds like the words are connected. The letters **s**, **z**, and **x** all sound like a **z** when connected to the following words.

nous étudions   les enfants   mon oncle
vous avez   deux élèves   leurs amis

Sometimes you will have a *liaison* multiple times in a single sentence. Try saying these sentences out loud, deciding where there should be a *liaison*.

Vous avez trois oncles?   Mon époux a des ordinateurs américains.

Mes amis habitent à Lourdes.   Ils ont des enfants?

Watch the video in Explorer and listen to François say these examples. Then watch the video again and practice saying the phrases with him.

Poitiers, Nouvelle-Aquitaine, France

J'avance 1

Voici ma famille

▶️ 🧭 Étape 1: Regardez

Ariane is a peer-mentor at your school for new students who speak French. As a part of her application, she created a video describing her family. Using the names she texted to you, watch the video, paying attention to the relationships between the different family members. Record your answers in the ***représentation schématique*** in Explorer.

✉️ 🧭 Étape 2: Lisez et écrivez

Respond to Ariane's text message from ***Étape 1***, noting what you understood about who makes up her family and their names. Include any additional information if possible.

🎤 🧭 Étape 3: Présentez

You are applying for the same peer-mentor program at your school and the application process also requires you to make a video about your family and/or other important people and/or pets in your life. Include at least four different people and/or pets and their relationship to you. Record your video in Explorer after you have practiced and remember that all materials for ***J'avance 1*** can be found in Explorer.

🧭 Mon progrès communicatif

I can identify family members when I hear someone talk about his or her family.

🧭 Mon progrès communicatif

I can respond to questions to provide information and simple details about family members.

🧭 Mon progrès communicatif

I can present information about family members, using a few simple details.

Comment dit-on? 2

 Comment sont les membres de ma famille?

 Voici des photos d'amis et de membres de la famille de Marianne.

Ce sont ma **jeune** cousine Élodie, qui a huit ans, et mon oncle Jean. Elle est très **courageuse**. Il est **patient**. Ils sont **beaux**, non?

Mes amis sont super **gentils**! Ils sont **canadiens** et très **actifs**!

Mon **petit** frère joue avec notre **grand** chien.

Ma grand-mère est **âgée** (elle a soixante-dix ans). Elle est **française** et elle est très **créative** et **généreuse**!

Ma tante, Carole, est **blonde**. Mon oncle, Amadou, et mes cousins sont **bruns**. Mon cousin, Florian, a seize ans et il est très **intelligent** et **ambitieux**. Carole et Amadou sont **québécois**.

Mon voisin est souvent **strict** et **méchant** envers son fils.

Mes deux chiens: Lourdaud est **grand** et **gros** et Pitchoun est **petit** et **mince**.

Mon **petit** chat Abricot est **roux** et très **mignon**.

Activité 12

✎ 🧭 Créons des mèmes

Jeanne is attempting to write captions for pictures for a website in French. She has asked for your help. Using adjectives from the box, complete each sentence describing the pictures. Pay careful attention to the placement of the adjectives!

petit	rousse	sérieux	jeune	gentille
	âgés	mignon	patient	

Que tu es fort!

Le _____ chien est _____.

Je suis un génie!

Le _____ garçon est _____.

Touche pas!

C'est ma langue!

La fille _____ est _____ avec le chien.

Activité 13

Quel âge ont-ils?

🎧 ✎ 🧭 Étape 1: Écoutez et écrivez

Listen to the friend of our blogger, Noah, as he shares the ages of some of his family members. Complete each sentence below with the number that you hear for each person's age.

1. Mon oncle, Jean, a _____ ans.

2. Ma grand-mère, Caroline, a _____ ans.

3. Mon grand-père, Stéphane, a _____ ans.

4. Ma mère, Claire, a _____ ans.

5. Mon beau-père, Paul, a _____ ans.

6. Mon demi-frère, Emmanuel, a _____ ans.

7. L'arrière-grand-mère de mon meilleur ami a _____ ans!

8. Moi, j'ai _____ ans.

Comment dit-on?

🧭 Les numéros de 70 à 100

In previous chapters, you learned numbers up to 69. The patterns you have thus far seen change a bit starting at 70.

70 soixante-dix
71 soixante et onze
72 soixante-douze
73 soixante-treize

…

80 quatre-vingts
81 quatre-vingt-un
82 quatre-vingt-deux

90 quatre-vingt-dix
91 quatre-vingt-onze
92 quatre-vingt-douze

100 cent

Mon progrès communicatif

I can share information about the ages of some family members.

Mon progrès communicatif

I can ask and answer questions about characteristics of family members or friends.

Stratégies

▶ Interpersonal Speaking

It can be intimidating to speak another language when you are just starting to learn it. However, here are some helpful tips to practice.

1. Talk about familiar topics.

2. Show pictures to help you get your point across.

3. Make comments and ask questions to keep the conversation going.

Watch the Interpersonal Speaking Strategies video in your Explorer course for more examples and tips.

🎙 ✦ Étape 2: Parlez

Now, it is your turn to share the ages of some family members. Select five people in a family, state their ages as Noah's friend did in **Étape 1**, and record yourself sharing this information in Explorer.

Activité 14

Nos caractéristiques

📖 ✦ Étape 1: Lisez et écrivez

Complete each sentence below with an activity that the person described is likely to enjoy doing.

Modèle

Je suis sportif. J'aime faire du sport.

1. Elle est sérieuse. Elle aime _____.

2. Tu es créatif. Tu aimes _____.

3. Il est timide. Il n'aime pas _____.

4. Elle est sociable. Elle aime _____.

5. Je suis bavarde. J'adore _____.

💬 ✦ Étape 2: Parlez

With a **partenaire**, ask each other about the characteristics of family members or friends, then answer by stating what that person likes or does not like to do.

Modèle

Élève A: Ta tante est paresseuse?

Élève B: Oui! Elle déteste travailler./Non, elle travaille beaucoup!

Ask a question to keep a conversation going.

Activité 15

Comment suis-je?

💬 Étape 1: Parlez

You are meeting up with your classmate's best friend to get help with an assignment, but you have never met. You ask your classmate what his or her friend looks like and your classmate will answer either positively or negatively. Use the **modèle** as a guide.

Modèle

Élève A: Est-ce que ton ami(e) est brun(e)?

Élève B: Oui, il/elle est brun(e).

Non, il/elle n'est pas brun(e). Il/elle est blond(e).

✉️ 🧭 Étape 2: Écrivez

To ensure a successful rendezvous, your classmate provides his or her best friend with your cell phone number. When you receive his or her text message, you will respond with a description of yourself. There should be a minimum of five descriptors in this message.

Rappel

américain/américaine
bilingue
sérieux/sérieuse
sportif/sportive

On peut aussi dire

amusant(e)	*funny*
bavard(e)	*talkative*
célibataire	*single*
divorcé(e)	*divorced*
énergique	*energetic*
marié(e)	*married*
paresseux/ paresseuse	*lazy*
sociable	*sociable*
timide	*shy*

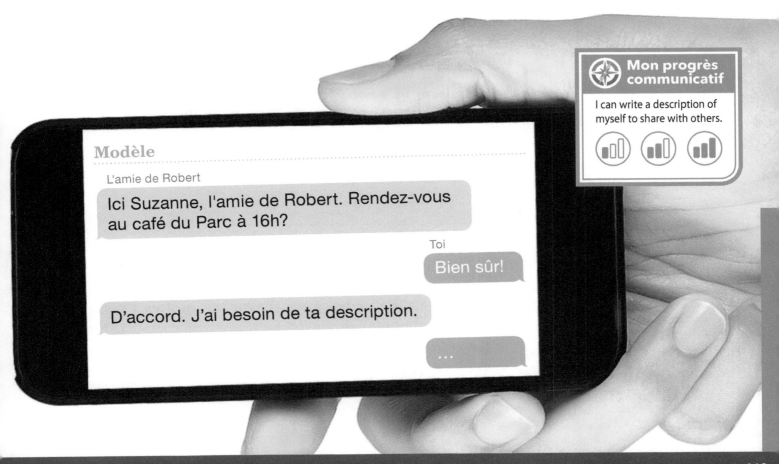

🧭 **Mon progrès communicatif**

I can write a description of myself to share with others.

Modèle

L'amie de Robert

Ici Suzanne, l'amie de Robert. Rendez-vous au café du Parc à 16h?

Toi
Bien sûr!

D'accord. J'ai besoin de ta description.

...

Zoom culture

Pratique culturelle: Le Pacs et le mariage en France

  Connexions

How are the perspectives of a region or county mirrored in the options available to couples?

In France, individuals have options for legally committing to each other. One option is *le mariage*, as is possible in other countries. Another option is for couples to enter into a *Pacte civil de solidarité*, or *Pacs*, which is a contract much like marriage, but that has different obligations for the couple. One significant difference between the two involves the ability to adopt a child. With a *Pacs*, the couple cannot adopt a child, unless they do so as individuals; but with marriage, adoption is possible as a couple. The *Pacs* has been incredibly popular in France, as shown by this graph, which depicts the evolution of the number of *Pacs* and marriages since the *Pacs* first became an option for couples in 1999.

  Réflexion

Research some of the similarities and differences between a traditional marriage and the *Pacs* in France. How is family structure affected by the *Pacs*? Provide your answers in the discussion forum in Explorer.

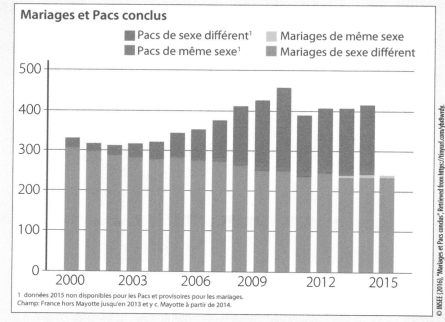

Mariages et Pacs conclus

- Pacs de sexe différent[1]
- Pacs de même sexe[1]
- Mariages de même sexe
- Mariages de sexe différent

1 données 2015 non disponibles pour les Pacs et provisoires pour les mariages.
Champ: France hors Mayotte jusqu'en 2013 et y c. Mayotte à partir de 2014.

© INSEE (2016), "Mariages et Pacs conclus", Retrieved from https://tinyurl.com/ybt6wrdy.

 Mon progrès interculturel

I can identify some legal practices related to traditional marriages and civil contracts between two people in France.

Réflexion interculturelle

Research marriages and civil unions in other Francophone countries and in your region. Is there anything similar to the *Pacs* in the area where you live? Provide the information requested or answer the questions in the discussion forum in Explorer.

Paris, France

Découvrons 2

Describing Family Members

Ma cousine Sophie est **jeune** et **gentille**.

Mes parents sont **intelligents** et **patients**.

Mon cousin Raoul est **mince** et **patient**.

Mon oncle Robert est un peu **gros** et **gentil**.

Jean-Paul est le plus **jeune** petit-fils de mes grands-parents.

Ma tante Juliette est **grande** et **créative**.

Je suis **brune** et **grande**.

Ma grand-mère est **âgée**.

Découvertes

Look at the words in bold that Christelle uses to describe the members of her family. What do you observe about the different forms? Can you figure out when to use **gentil** vs. **gentille**? **Grand** vs. **grande**? **Patient** vs. **patients**? Discuss these examples with your classmates and teacher, view the **Découvrons 2** resources in Explorer, and check the **Synthèse de grammaire** at the end of this unit.

Activité 16

Comment sont-ils?

📖 🧭 **Étape 1**

Combine an expression from the left-hand column with a description from the right-hand column to make sentences that Noah could say about his family. ***ATTENTION!*** The descriptions are possible only if they agree in gender and number and, for some items, more than one response can be correct.

1. Ma famille
2. Mes grands-parents
3. Mes cousines
4. Mon oncle
5. Ma grande-mère
6. Mon chat Pierre

a. est gentil
b. sont âgés
c. est stricte
d. est grande
e. sont intelligentes
f. est créatif
g. sont patients
h. est petit
i. sont belles
j. est mignon

✏️ 🧭 **Étape 2**

Write original sentences similar to the ones that were formed in ***Étape 1*** to describe either your own family, an imagined family, or even a famous family. Use vocabulary from ***Comment dit-on 1 & 2*** as well as ***On peut aussi dire*** or look up any additional words needed. Make sure that each sentence contains descriptive adjectives that agree in number and gender with the nouns.

Expressions utiles

Here are some expressions to help you be more descriptive in using adjectives. These expressions always go before the adjective.

Mon cousin est **vraiment** (*really*) grand.

Ta mère est **si** (*so*) gentille.

Mes grands-parents sont **toujours** (*always*) patients.

Leur chat est **trop** (*too*) mignon!

Other expressions that modify adjectives are **rarement** (*rarely*), **assez** (*rather*), and **souvent** (*often*).

Rappel

Le verbe être

As you have noticed, the most commonly used verb in French is often used with adjectives as in phrases like these: ***Mon cousin Paul est ambitieux***; or, ***Mes grands-parents sont gentils***. Let's take a look at all forms of this verb:

je suis	nous sommes
tu es	vous êtes
il/elle est	ils/elles sont

Activité 17

🎧 ✦ De qui parle-t-on?

Listen to Océane describe different members of her family. Of the four possibilities below, whom could she be referring to? Listen carefully to the gender and the number of the adjectives to figure it out. Write both the letter of the person(s) being described and the adjective used to describe him, her, or them.

a. La tante Pauline

b. L'oncle Georges

c. Les grands-parents

d. Les cousines Delphine et Caroline

Modèle

(You hear) *Il est actif.*   (refers to) b. L'oncle Georges

1. _____ 2. _____ 3. _____

4. _____ 5. _____ 6. _____

Activité 18

Décrivons la famille

✏️ 💬 ✦ Étape 1: Écrivez et parlez

Imagine that three of these photos represent members of your family. For each photo, write simple sentences: one sentence identifies who that person is (using *c'est/ce sont*) and a second sentence describes that person (those people) using two adjectives (using *il/elle est* or *ils/elles sont*). Compare your sentences with those of an *autre élève dans la classe*.

Modèle (photo#1)

C'est mon cousin. Il est créatif et gentil.

💬 Étape 2: Parlez

Working with a *partenaire*, ask each other who the people are in the three photos that you have chosen and provide responses that identify their relationship to you and describe them using at least one adjective.

Modèle

Élève 1: Qui est-ce?

Élève 2: C'est ma cousine. Elle est sportive.

La description d'une famille

You will write a description of a famous family. This family could be an actual family (past or present) or from a film, a television show, a novel, or other source. Your teacher will read the descriptions out loud to see if the class can guess the famous family.

✏️ 💬 ✺ Étape 1: Préparez

Working with a *partenaire* or small group, create your description by writing out the answers to the following questions. Do not use any names or other obvious information.

1. Combien de personnes est-ce qu'il y a dans la famille?
2. Qui sont-ils? (un père, une mère)
3. Quel âge a chaque *(each)* personne?
4. Comment sont les membres de la famille? Utilisez des adjectifs.

🎧 ✺ Étape 2: Écoutez

Now listen to the family descriptions. Can you identify the family being described?

Détail grammatical

C'est vs. Il/Elle est

C'est (plural form is *ce sont*) and *il/elle est* (plural forms are *ils/elles sont*) are two very common expressions used to introduce and describe people and things. Since these expressions can both mean "he/she/it is" or "they are," the best way to choose which expression to use is this: *c'est (ce sont)* will be followed by a noun.

Voilà Paul. C'est mon cousin.
There's Paul. He is my cousin.

Voilà Paul. Il est grand.
There's Paul. He is tall.

Mon progrès communicatif

I can write a description of myself to share with others.

Mon progrès communicatif

I can identify which person is being described.

J'avance 2

Mon/ma correspondant(e)

 ### Étape 1: Écrivez

Your French teacher is establishing an e-pal program with adolescents from the French region of *La Nouvelle-Aquitaine* for your French class. Write an email to a prospective correspondent in which you describe yourself. Ask questions about your future e-pal and his or her family.

 ### Étape 2: Regardez

In Explorer, you will see a series of sentences describing potential e-pals from France followed by photos of these same young people. Match the sentences with the photos.

💬 ✤ Étape 3: Parlez

In a round table discussion with *un petit groupe*, ask and answer questions about each other's family or about the family pictured at the beginning of the *Découvrons 2* section. This exchange of information should include such items as number of members in immediate or extended family, names, ages, and descriptions of family members. All of the materials for *J'avance 2* can be found in Explorer.

Mon progrès communicatif

I can ask and answer questions about characteristics of family members or friends.

Comment dit-on? 3

✤ **Chez moi**

J'habite dans...

une maison

un appartement dans
un immeuble

Ma maison est...

en ville

à la campagne

Ma maison a...

une cuisine

une salle à manger

un salon

une salle de bains

des toilettes

une chambre à coucher

un balcon

un jardin

un garage

Activité 20

Où dans la maison?

📝 ✦ Étape 1: Écrivez

List the parts of the house where you generally do each activity.

1. étudier
2. manger
3. parler au téléphone
4. regarder des films
5. jouer d'un instrument de musique
6. jouer aux jeux vidéo
7. surfer sur internet
8. danser
9. être seul(e) (*alone*)
10. être avec la famille

💬 ⓪ ✦ Étape 2: Comparez

Compare your answers from ***Étape 1*** with a ***partenaire*** by asking and answering questions.

Modèle

Élève A: Où est-ce que tu étudies?

Élève B: J'étudie dans ma chambre.

Activité 21

Un nouvel appartement

🎧 ✦ Étape 1: Écoutez

Suzanne has just moved into a new apartment and she describes it in the conversation with her cousin Éric, who lives on the island of Guadeloupe. Listen and indicate which elements on the list she mentions.

____ une salle de bains   ____ une salle à manger

____ une cuisine   ____ la chambre de Suzanne

____ le garage   ____ le balcon

On peut aussi dire

une buanderie
laundry, utility room

un bureau
desk

un canapé
couch, sofa

une chaise
chair

une commode
dresser

un lit
bed

un placard
closet

une table
table

🎧 ✹ **Étape 2: Réécoutez**

Listen again and note any adjectives that Suzanne uses to describe elements of her new apartment in the *représentation schématique*.

Activité 22

La maison de Claire

▶️ ✏️ ✹ **Étape 1: Regardez et anticipez**

Watch (without the sound) Claire, *la tante* of our blogger Jeanne, as she gives a video tour of her apartment. Write down as many details in French as you can about what you think she may be saying.

▶️ ✹ **Étape 2: Regardez et vérifiez**

Now watch and listen to Claire's tour to see how many details you were able to predict in *Étape 1*.

Activité 23

Les activités en vacances

Les activités préférées des Français pendant leurs vacances
Vous personnellement, qu'aimez-vous faire en priorité en vacances?

Activité	%
Faire des balades	33%
Dormir/se reposer	15%
Visiter un site culturel	15%
Faire de bons repas	9%
Bronzer	6%
Bricoler/jardiner	5%
Faire des rencontres	5%
Faire la fête	4%
Lire	3%
Faire du sport	2%
Faire du shopping	1%
Jouer à des jeux de société	1%
Regarder la télévision	1%

📖 ✥ Étape 1:Lisez

You were reading some French blogs to learn more about preferred vacation activities and found this infographic. With a **partenaire**, work together to understand all the activities listed. Record your preferences and those of your **partenaire** in the **représentation schématique**.

moi	nous deux	mon/ma partenaire

📖 ✉ ✥ Étape 2: Répondez

In the comment section of the blog, the authors have asked readers to respond to the survey question: **Vous personnellement, qu'aimez-vous faire en priorité en vacances?** Add your top three activity preferences to the class discussion forum for this **étape**. You can include activities from the list or other activities you know in French. Then, respond to other entries with a question or an **Expression utile**.

⊕ ✥ Étape 3: Comparez

Compare the preferences listed in the discussion forum to the preferences identified in the chart. How are the activity preferences similar and or different? Use the **représentation schématique** to help you compare the information.

Dordogne, France

Zoom culture

Produit culturel: Les bâtiments et le logement

 Connexions

How do we describe the structure of buildings and houses in our community in comparison to how it is done in the Francophone world? Can you recognize signs important in everyday life?

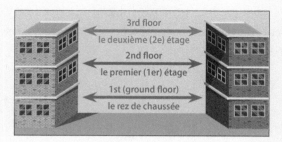

3rd floor	le deuxième (2e) étage
2nd floor	le premier (1er) étage
1st (ground floor)	le rez de chaussée

Knowing how to refer to the various parts of buildings in the French-speaking world is an important skill. The most significant difference is the names given to the various floors of buildings. What you would call the ground or first floor in your community is called *le rez de chaussée* in many Francophone countries. The second floor is called *le premier étage* and the third floor is called *le deuxième étage*.

In many French apartment buildings, *le rez de chaussée* is the level where the *concierge* (*caretaker/superintendent*) would live.

Having a working knowledge of these signs is a necessary aspect of your time in Francophone regions. Public bathrooms are referred to as *toilettes* or *WC* as compared to *la salle de bains* or *la salle d'eau*, which are found in one's home. At the far right is one of 420 *sanisettes* found in Paris. These automated public bathrooms feature self-cleaning toilets and doors that automatically open and close.

Mon progrès interculturel

I can identify how signage in public buildings and spaces in Francophone cultures is similar to and different from that in my culture.

⊙⊙ ✷ **Réflexion**

Research how the term *rez de chaussée* came to mean the ground floor. What is the difference in the role of the *concierge* in a French apartment building as opposed to that person's role in an American hotel? Provide your answers in the discussion forum in Explorer.

Tu fais quoi en famille?

✏ ✦ Étape 1: Identifiez

You are responsible for categorizing the following photos of Francophone families for an online database. Write three or four words or short phrases that could be used to tag each image.

Modèle

Mon progrès communicatif

I can write descriptions of the places and activities that bring families together in my culture and in Francophone cultures.

regarder un film

famille

cinéma

1

2

3

4

5

✏ ✦ Étape 2: Écrivez

Choose one image from *Étape 1* and write a detailed description of the activity, location, and people. Be sure to use a variety of vocabulary and expressions that you have learned.

Découvrons 3

Asking Informational Questions

Salut, Claude! Tu as une grande famille!
Où est-ce que tu habites avec tes parents?

Nous habitons à <u>Biarritz dans une maison</u>.

Ton cousin Raoul habite **où**?

Il habite <u>un appartement à Paris</u> avec sa famille.

Combien de chambres est-ce qu'il y a dans l'appartement de Raoul?

Il y a <u>deux</u> chambres.

Et dans la maison de ta grand-mère, il y a **combien** de chambres?

Il y a <u>trois</u> chambres.

Des appartements dans un immeuble à Paris, en France.

Découvertes

📹 📖 ✦ Observe the words in bold that Claude's friend uses to ask him questions about his family. What do you observe about the different forms? What do you notice about how questions can be formed in French and where you see **où** or **combien** in a question? Discuss your hypotheses with your classmates and teacher. Also be sure to look at the **Découvrons 3** resources in Explorer and the **Synthèse de grammaire** at the end of this unit to find out more.

Une maison individuelle à Biarritz, en France.

Activité 25

Comment est-ce que nous formons des questions?

📖 ✦ **Étape 1: Lisez**

Find out more about Claude's family, whom you have met in *Découvrons 2* and *3*. Match the questions to the answer. There may be two questions for one answer.

1. Où est-ce qu'il habite?

2. Qu'est-ce que Sophie aime faire?

3. Comment est sa cousine Sophie?

4. Sophie aime faire quoi?

5. Il habite où?

6. Qui est sa tante?

7. À quel étage est-ce que Raoul habite?

8. Dans quelle ville habite la grand-mère de Claude?

9. Raoul habite à quel étage?

10. Pourquoi est-ce que Raoul habite à Paris?

A. Sa grand-mère habite à Biarritz.

B. Claude habite à Biarritz, en France.

C. Elle est gentille.

D. Juliette

E. Parce qu'il adore les grandes villes

F. Au 2ᵉ étage

G. Elle aime lire dans sa chambre.

Rappel

Les mots interrogatifs

Remember these questions that you asked and answered in *Unité 1*? Keeping them in mind will help you create new questions in this unit.

Comment ça va?

D'**où** viens-tu?

Quelle est la date?

Quel âge as-tu?

C'est **quand** ton anniversaire?

Qu'est-ce que tu aimes étudier?

Pourquoi tu étudies le français?

Qui est ton professeur?

Est-ce que tu aimes le français?

Expressions utiles

C'est génial!
That's awesome!

D'accord!
Ok!

Je ne sais pas!
I don't know!

Je sais!
I know!

Vachement cool!
Really cool!

Mon progrès communicatif

I can ask and answer questions about a family home.

Détail grammatical

Le mot combien

Combien is a handy question word for amounts, to ask either how much or how many of something. It is usually used along with other words that represent the objects or people being counted. It is often used in combination with **il y a** (*there is/there are*).

Look at these questions to see if you can figure out what is being asked:

Combien de chaises est-ce qu'il y a dans le salon?

Il y a **combien de chaises** dans le salon?

Tu as **combien de frères**?

Combien de frères est-ce que tu as?

Étape 2: Demandez et répondez

Now ask a **partenaire** a few different questions about a familiar home. Use the ideas below to help you form the questions. Remember to try out different ways of forming the questions and to react to the answers with a comment from the **Expressions utiles** or another expression that you know.

Modèle

Élève A: Combien de personnes habitent ta maison?

Élève B: Quatre personnes habitent ma maison.

Élève A: C'est intéressant! Dans ma maison aussi!

Here are some ideas to ask your **partenaire**:

- name of city or town
- house or apartment (which floor?)
- why he or she likes/dislikes where he or she lives
- how many rooms (and names of the rooms)
- activities that bring families together in different rooms

Activité 26

Une chambre d'hôtel

Étape 1: Préparez

Your grandmother is flying to Martinique for a vacation and needs to reserve a hotel room, but has asked you to call the hotel to get some information on available rooms. Since you know her well, you understand her specific needs and have jotted them down on a piece of paper so you remember what to ask the hotel:

- She uses a wheelchair, so she needs to have an elevator.
- She loves high floors because of the view.
- She likes to have just one bed.

Prepare the questions that you will need to ask to ensure that she gets the best room for her particular needs.

 **Étape 2: Appelez**

You are now ready to call the hotel, but when you call, you are greeted by a recorded message asking you to leave a message including your name and telephone number. Record your message in Explorer.

Activité 27

Les vacances de famille

 **Étape 1: Lisez et écrivez**

Imagine that you hosted a student from the city of Bordeaux. Having heard so much about this area of France, you are planning a trip to the southwest of France this summer. You have asked your host student to look through local newspapers for a suitable rental property for your stay. He found this ad that may be suitable. Time is of the essence, so you send a **texto** (*text message*) to your friend to ask questions about this property.

I can understand online descriptions of rental properties.

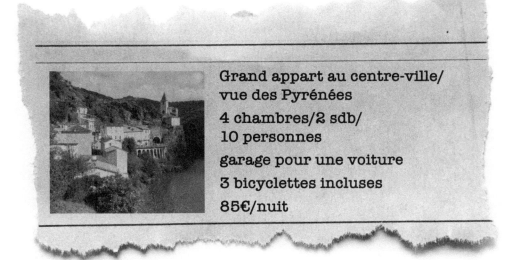

Grand appart au centre-ville/
vue des Pyrénées

4 chambres/2 sdb/
10 personnes

garage pour une voiture

3 bicyclettes incluses

85€/nuit

I can ask appropriate questions to inquire about a rental property in a Francophone country.

 **Étape 2: Invitez**

Now that you have selected a rental property for your upcoming vacation, you have been asked to invite an aunt, who only speaks French and whom you do not get to see very often, to join you on this vacation. Write her an email describing the rental property and inviting her to join you on this vacation.

I can write a description of a rental property in a Francophone country.

J'avance 3

Cherchez une location de vacances

📖 🧭 **Étape 1: Lisez et choisissez**

You and your friends or family are planning on renting a house or an apartment near Sherbrooke, Quebec for a few days so that you can visit this beautiful city over the summer and practice speaking French. In Explorer, you will find listings from a rental property website. Select the one that you feel would best meet your group's needs and explain your reasoning using the **modèle** as a guide.

Modèle

L'appartement à _____ est parfait parce qu' il
_____.

💬 ✦ Étape 2: Demandez

Now that you have selected the rental property that best fits your family's or friends' needs, you need to seek more information to ensure that this property will be perfect for your family or friends. When you call the rental company, you get their voicemail. Record a message in Explorer asking questions that would help you gain a better understanding of all that is offered by the property that interests you. Be sure to introduce yourself and to leave a telephone number so that they can return your call!

Mon progrès communicatif

I can ask appropriate questions to inquire about a rental property in a Francophone country.

📝 ✦ Étape 3: Évaluez

Upon returning from your vacation, you decide to write an online *appréciation* (*a review*) of your thoughts on the property to share with future renters. In order to ensure that the review is helpful, be sure to be specific!

All of the materials for *J'avance 3* can be found in Explorer.

☆ ☆ ☆ ☆ ☆

Titre

Appréciation

Soumettre

Mon progrès communicatif

I can write a description of a rental property in a Francophone country.

Mauricie, Québec, Canada

Synthèse de grammaire

1. Indicating Family Relationships: *Les adjectifs possessifs*

Possessive adjectives help us designate ownership and take the place of articles.

un frère = *a brother*   **mon** frère = *my brother*

la calculatrice = *the calculator*   **ma** calculatrice = *my calculator*

The form of the possessive is determined by the person or object "owned".

She has her calculator in her backpack.
Elle a **sa** calculatrice dans **son** sac à dos.

He has his calculator in his backpack.
Il a **sa** calculatrice dans **son** sac à dos.

possessive	masc./fem./plural	possessive	singular/plural
my	mon, ma, mes	our	notre, nos
your	ton, ta, tes	your	votre, vos
his/her	son, sa, ses	their	leur, leurs

The French language goes to great lengths to maintain a fluid sound. If you wanted to talk about a friend who is a female, rules would dictate that you would come up with **ma amie**. However, the correct structure is **mon amie** because **ma amie** features consecutive vowels, which sounds much less fluid than **mon amie**.

Le verbe avoir

The verb **avoir** is one of the most frequently used verbs in French and means "to have."

Le verbe **avoir**

j'ai	nous avons
tu as	vous avez
il/elle a	ils/elles ont

Tu as des frères et des sœurs?   *Do you have brothers and sisters?*
Oui, j'ai une sœur.   *Yes, I have a sister.*

2. Describing Family Members: *Les adjectifs*

Most French adjectives have four forms, for example:

Masculine singular	grand	Masculine plural	grand**s**
Feminine singular	grand**e**	Feminine plural	grand**es**

Adjectives that end in *-e* only have two endings (*-e, -es*); they do not distinguish between masculine and feminine, but show only plural agreement:

Ma sœur est **jeune**. Mon frère est **jeune** aussi. Mes grands-parents ne sont pas **jeunes**.

Some adjective groups display unique patterns.

masculine	**feminine**
canadien	canadienne
courageux	courageuse
créatif	créative
gentil	gentille
gros	grosse

3. Asking Informational Questions: *Les questions*

The French language offers more than just one way to structure questions. Here are many of the essential interrogatives to form questions: *comment, quand, où, pourquoi, qu'est-ce que, à quelle heure, qui.*

To ask someone with whom they like to chat, the options are:

1) Avec *qui* est-ce que tu aimes discuter?

2) Tu aimes discuter avec *qui*?

The two formulas that you have seen are as follows:

1) interrogative + *est-ce que* + subject + verb

2) subject + verb + interrogative

Asking questions with *combien*

Combien is a useful question word that can mean either "how much" or "how many." It is used with the preposition *de* followed by a noun that can refer to either people or objects. It is often used with the expression *il y a*.

Combien d'oncles est-ce que tu as?
Tu utilises **combien de cahiers**?
Combien de musique est-ce qu'il y a dans ta tablette?

Vocabulaire

Comment dit-on? 1: I can identify members of my family.

Les membres de la famille	*Family Members*
le cousin/la cousine	*cousin*
l'enfant (m. or f.)	*child*
la fille	*daughter*
le fils	*son*
le frère	*brother*
la grand-mère	*grandmother*
le grand-père	*grandfather*
les grands-parents (m. pl.)	*grandparents*
la mère	*mother*
l'oncle (m.)	*uncle*
les parents (m. pl.)	*parents*
le père	*father*
la sœur	*sister*
la tante	*aunt*

Comment dit-on? 2: I can describe members of my family.

Les adjectifs	*Adjectives*	Les adjectifs	*Adjectives*
actif/active	*active*	grand/grande	*tall*
âgé/âgée	*old*	gros/grosse	*fat, big*
ambitieux/ambitieuse	*ambitious*	intelligent/intelligente	*smart, intelligent*
beau/belle	*beautiful*	jeune	*young*
blond/blonde	*blond*	méchant/méchante	*mean*
brun/brune	*brunette*	mignon/mignonne	*cute*
canadien/canadienne	*Canadian*	mince	*thin*
courageux/courageuse	*courageous*	patient/patiente	*patient*
créatif/créative	*creative*	petit/petite	*small, short*
français/française	*French*	québécois/québécoise	*from Quebec*
généreux/généreuse	*generous*	roux/rousse	*red-headed*
gentil/gentille	*nice, kind*	strict/stricte	*strict, firm*

Les numéros de 70 à 100	*Numbers 70 through 100*
soixante-dix	*70*
soixante et onze	*71*
soixante-douze	*72*
soixante-treize	*73*
...	
quatre-vingts	*80*
quatre-vingt-un	*81*
quatre-vingt-deux	*82*
...	
quatre-vingt-dix	*90*
quatre-vingt-onze	*91*
quatre-vingt-douze	*92*
...	
cent	*100*

Comment dit-on? 3: I can describe where I live.

Chez moi	*My house*
l'appartement (m.)	*apartment*
le balcon	*balcony*
la campagne	*countryside*
la chambre à coucher	*bedroom*
la cuisine	*kitchen*
le garage	*garage*
l'immeuble (m.)	*apartment building*
le jardin	*garden*
la maison	*house*
la salle à manger	*dining room*
la salle de bains	*bathroom*
le salon	*living room*
les toilettes (f. pl.)	*WC, toilets*
la ville	*city*

Expressions utiles	
assez	*rather*
rarement	*rarely*
si	*so*
souvent	*often*
toujours	*always*
trop	*too*
vraiment	*really*

J'y arrive

Questions essentielles

- Who are the members of a family?
- Which attributes and interests do family members share?
- Which places and activities bring families together in our culture and in Francophone cultures?

Une nouvelle famille, une nouvelle culture

You have another opportunity to participate in an *échange scolaire* through the website *jeveuxapprendredeslangues.com*. The following assessments are based on the ads and blogs posted by Jeanne, Ariane, and Noah. Before you begin, refer to the *J'y arrive* rubric in Explorer to familiarize yourself with the evaluation criteria.

Interpretive Assessment

◼️ ✦ Ma famille d'échange

Jeanne, Ariane, and Noah are looking to improve their English by participating in an exchange program with an English-speaking host family. Watch all three of their videos and use the chart of attributes in Explorer to take notes on the three bloggers and their families.

Choose which blogger you are going to host and compare him or her to yourself using the *diagramme de Venn*.

Interpersonal Assessment

  Une conversation avec Jeanne, Ariane ou Noah.

You have selected which person you would like to host as part of the summer exchange. Both of you have arranged to speak on the phone at 4:00 p.m. your local time (France is six hours ahead of Eastern time in the U.S. and Rwanda is seven hours ahead of Eastern time in the U.S.). You have agreed to speak in French for this telephone call. In order to prepare for the call, a *partenaire* and you will practice asking and answering questions about your families.

Presentational Assessment

 Voici ma famille!

Create a digital album to share written information and photographs about your family, important people and/or pets, and home to make your exchange student feel comfortable when he or she visits.

Can-Do Statements

Unité préliminaire

Mon progrès communicatif

❏ 📖 I can identify and name places on a map where French is spoken around the world. (9)

❏ 🎧 I can understand some basic words and phrases when a French speaker introduces him or herself. (14)

❏ 💬 I can answer questions about my name, how I am, and where I am from. (17)

❏ 💬 I can ask and answer questions to meet and greet a young person. (17)

❏ 📹 I can follow classroom commands. (19)

❏ 💬 I can say the date, the day of the week, the month of the year, and my birthday. (21)

❏ 🎧 I can recognize and use numbers to express phone numbers. (25)

❏ 📹 I can recognize some words related to activities in a promotional video. (29)

❏ 📖 I can identify the purpose of an advertisement. (31)

Mon progrès interculturel

❏ I can identify some familiar products, landmarks, and monuments and what they represent to the Francophone people. (11)

❏ I can identify appropriate expressions and practices, such as gestures and body language, associated with greetings, introductions, and leave-taking in Francophone cultures. (16)

❏ I can identify how Francophone cultures and my culture celebrate local and national holidays or festivals. (30)

❏ I can identify the ways people say numbers for the calendar year in French and in English. (35)

Unité 1

Mon progrès communicatif

❏ 💬 I can ask and answer simple questions about identity. (48, 53, 55)

❏ 📖 I can understand words relating to identity to describe myself and others. (49)

❏ 🖊 I can write some simple sentences about identity. (54)

❏ 📖 I can understand some words and phrases relating to activity preferences. (57)

❏ 💬 I can ask and answer questions about activities that I like and dislike. (59)

❏ 📖 I can identify key words and some information in an online ad for a summer camp. (62)

❏ 🖊 I can write simple sentences about myself and activities that I like and I don't like. (63, 66, 68)

❏ 🎤 I can introduce myself and provide some basic information about my identity. (64, 68)

❏ 🎧 I can understand information related to identity and preferences. (71, 80)

❏ 💬 I can ask and answer questions to get to know another person. (71, 81)

Mon progrès interculturel

❏ I can identify some similarities and differences between Francophone young people and myself. (45, 80)

❏ I can identify some famous French speakers, their professions, and their contributions. (51)

❏ I can identify popular sports in Quebec and France and how they are similar to or different from sports in my community. (59)

❏ I can identify musical events and musicians in a Francophone region and how they are the same or different from those in my community. (73)

❏ I can identify other languages spoken in my community and what they represent to people. (79)

Unité 2

Mon progrès communicatif

❏ 🎦 I can understand when someone names school supplies. (95, 104)

❏ 💬 I can respond to questions relating to school supplies. (97, 105)

❏ ✏️ I can write a list of school supplies. (98)

❏ 🎧 I can understand some basic activities and objects related to specific classes. (107)

❏ 🎦 I can understand the names of classes and how many hours per week they meet. (108)

❏ 💬 I can ask and answer questions about my class preferences. (111, 117)

❏ 💬 I can exchange information about my school schedule. (114)

❏ ✏️ I can provide information about my school schedule using the 24-hour clock. (115, 117)

❏ 📖🎧🎦 I can identify common student activities and locations at school. (120, 124, 132)

❏ 💬 I can ask and answer questions about typical activities during the school day. (122, 131)

❏ ✏️ I can identify some activities that students like to do at school. (122)

❏ ✉️ I can respond to an email from a Francophone student about typical activities during the school day. (129, 133)

❏ 🎤 I can create a video blog about my daily activities at school. (131)

Mon progrès interculturel

❏ I can identify some similarities and differences between a Francophone teen and myself related to school life. (93)

❏ I can identify some information about grade levels in a Francophone country and how students' grades are recorded. (100)

❏ I can identify what Francophone students do in their free time at school, where they go, and why. (110)

❏ I can identify some simple similarities and differences between my schedule and that of a Francophone student. (115, 116)

❏ I can identify practices and related perspectives regarding the use of technology in schools in Francophone countries. (123)

Unité 3

Mon progrès communicatif

❏ ▶️ I can identify family members when I hear someone talk about his or her family. (149, 159)

❏ 🎧 I can identify the actions of family members in a **comptine**, a French nursery rhyme. (150)

❏ 💬 I can ask and answer questions about family members in a photo. (156)

❏ 📧 I can respond to questions to provide information and simple details about family members. (157, 159)

❏ 🎤 I can present information about family members using a few simple details. (159)

❏ 🎤 I can share information about the ages of some family members. (162)

❏ 💬 I can ask and answer questions about characteristics of family members or friends. (162, 171)

❏ 📧 I can write a description of myself to share with others. (163, 170)

❏ 📖▶️ I can identify which person is being described. (168, 170)

❏ ▶️ I can understand simple descriptions of Francophone homes. (174)

❏ ✏️ I can write descriptions of the places and activities that bring families together in my culture and in Francophone cultures. (177)

❏ 💬 I can ask and answer questions about a family home. (180)

❏ 📖 I can understand online descriptions of rental properties. (181, 182)

❏ 💬 I can ask appropriate questions to inquire about a rental property in a Francophone country. (181, 183)

❏ ✏️ I can write a description of a rental property in a Francophone country. (181, 183)

Mon progrès interculturel

❏ I can identify some similarities and differences between a Francophone teen and myself related to preferences and place of origin. (145)

❏ I can identify whom people consider to be part of their family in my culture and in a Francophone culture. (153)

❏ I can identify some legal practices related to traditional marriages and civil contracts between two people in France. (164)

❏ I can identify how signage in public buildings and spaces in Francophone cultures is similar to and different from that in my culture. (176)

Rubrics
Level 1A *EntreCultures* **Analytic Growth Rubric**

Interpretive Reading, Listening, Audiovisual, and Viewing

Level 1A Target: Novice Low - Novice Mid

DOMAINS	NOVICE LOW	NOVICE MID	NOVICE HIGH
How well do I understand? *Main Idea and/or Details*	I can recognize a few words that are very familiar to me.	I can recognize and understand some basic information with memorized words and phrases.	I can identify pieces of information and sometimes the main idea(s) without explanation when the idea is familiar, short, and simple.
What words and structures do I understand? *Vocabulary and Structures in Context*	I can recognize a few very familiar words and phrases in text or speech from well-practiced topics.	I can recognize words and phrases, including cognates, and borrowed words in text or speech from well-practiced topics.	I can understand words, phrases, simple sentences, and some structures in short, simple texts or sentence-length speech, one utterance at a time, with support, related to familiar topics of study.
How well can I understand unfamiliar language? *Context Clues*	I can understand some very basic word-level meaning from short, simple authentic texts or speech on very familiar topics that include cognates and/or visual clues.	I can understand some basic meaning when authentic texts or speech on very familiar topics include cognates and/or visual clues.	I can understand basic meaning when short, non-complex authentic texts or speech include cognates and visual clues, on familiar topics.

DOMAINS	NOVICE LOW	NOVICE MID	NOVICE HIGH
How well can I infer meaning beyond what I read or hear? *Inferences*	I can make minimal inferences based on visual clues, organizational layout, inflection and/or body language.	I can make limited inferences based on visual clues, organizational layout, background knowledge, keywords, inflection and/or body language.	I can make a few inferences based on visual clues, organizational layout, background knowledge, keywords, inflection and/or body language.
How intercultural am I? *Interculturality* *Based on classroom tasks/ activities/intercultural reflections and outside classroom experiences.	I can recognize limited cultural products, practices, or perspectives including cultural behaviors and expressions, related to daily life.	I can identify a few cultural products, practices, or perspectives including cultural behaviors and expressions related to daily life.	I can identify some cultural products, practices, and perspectives, including cultural behaviors and expressions related to daily life.

Adapted from Jefferson County Public Schools World Languages: Performance Assessment Rubrics (Kentucky), Howard County Public Schools World Languages (Maryland).

Level 1A *EntreCultures* **Analytic Growth Rubric**

Interpersonal Communication: Speaking and Writing

Level 1A Target: Novice Low - Novice Mid

DOMAINS	NOVICE LOW	NOVICE MID	NOVICE HIGH
How well do I maintain the conversation? *Quality of Interaction*	I have great difficulty maintaining a conversation. I speak with frequent hesitation, pauses, and/or repetition.	I have some difficulty maintaining simple conversations. I mainly use isolated words and memorized phrases. I speak with frequent hesitation, pauses, and/or repetition.	I can participate in short social interactions by asking and answering simple questions and relying heavily on learned phrases and short or incomplete sentences. I speak with hesitation, pauses, and/or repetition.
What language/ words do I use? *Vocabulary in Context*	I can use a limited number of memorized words and expressions to identify common objects and actions.	I can use a limited number of highly practiced words and expressions to identify familiar objects and actions.	I can use learned words and phrases to interact with others in tasks and activities on familiar topics.
How do I use language? *Function and Text Type*	I can use memorized words for functions (actions) and isolated words as structures.	I can ask and respond to highly predictable questions with words, lists, and memorized phrases. I am beginning to communicate beyond the word level, but my errors often interfere with the message.	I can use phrases, simple sentences, and questions. I am beginning to create original sentences with simple details on familiar topics, but errors sometimes interfere with the message.

DOMAINS	NOVICE LOW	NOVICE MID	NOVICE HIGH
How well am I understood ? *Comprehensibility*	I am understood only with great effort by someone accustomed to a language learner.	I am somewhat understood by someone accustomed to a language learner.	I am often understood by someone accustomed to a language learner.
How well do I understand? *Comprehension*	I can understand some isolated words and expressions that I have memorized. I need continual repetition.	I can understand some familiar language, one phrase at a time. I rely on visual clues, repetition, and/ or a slowed rate of speech.	I can understand pieces of information and sometimes the main idea in straightforward language that uses familiar structures. I occasionally rely on visual clues, repetition, and/ or a slowed rate of speech.
How intercultural am I? *Interculturality* *Based on classroom tasks/ activities/intercultural reflections and outside classroom experiences.	I can apply my knowledge of cultural products, practices, and perspectives in order to interact with respect and understanding.	I can apply my knowledge of cultural products, practices, and perspectives in order to interact with respect and understanding.	I can apply my knowledge of cultural products, practices, and perspectives in order to interact with respect and understanding.

Adapted from Jefferson County Public Schools World Languages: Performance Assessment Rubrics (Kentucky), Howard County Public Schools World Languages (Maryland).

Level 1A *EntreCultures* Analytic Growth Rubric

Presentational Speaking

Level 1A Target: Novice Low - Novice Mid

DOMAINS	NOVICE LOW	NOVICE MID	NOVICE HIGH
What language/ words do I use? *Vocabulary in Context*	I can use a very limited number of isolated words that are repetitive.	I can use a limited number of words and expressions to identify objects and actions in familiar contexts.	I can use words and expressions that I have practiced to present familiar topics.
How do I use language? *Function and Text Type*	I can use some isolated words.	I can use highly predictable words, lists, and memorized phrases in very familiar contexts.	I can use phrases, simple sentences, and questions. I am beginning to create original sentences with some simple details in familiar contexts.
How well am I understood ? *Comprehensibility*	I am understood only with great effort by someone accustomed to a language learner.	I am somewhat understood by someone accustomed to a language learner.	I am often understood by someone accustomed to a language learner.
How accurate am I? *Structures*	I can use a limited number of memorized words for structures.	I can use memorized words and some basic structures with frequent errors.	I can use basic structures in present time with some errors, relying on memorized phrases.
How well do I deliver my message? *Delivery, Fluency, Visuals, Impact on Audience*	I can deliver my message with great difficulty, speaking with frequent hesitation, pauses, and/or repetition.	I can deliver my message using isolated words and memorized phrases, speaking with frequent hesitation, pauses, and/or repetition.	I can deliver my message by relying on learned phrases and short or incomplete sentences, speaking with hesitation, pauses, and/or repetition.
How intercultural am I? *Interculturality* *Based on classroom tasks/ activities/ intercultural reflections and outside classroom experiences.*	I can apply my knowledge of cultural products, practices, and perspectives in order to interact with respect and understanding.	I can apply my knowledge of cultural products, practices, and perspectives in order to interact with respect and understanding.	I can apply my knowledge of cultural products, practices, and perspectives in order to interact with respect and understanding.

Adapted from Jefferson County Public Schools World Languages: Performance Assessment Rubrics (Kentucky), Howard County Public Schools World Languages (Maryland).

Level 1A *EntreCultures* Analytic Growth Rubric

Presentational Writing

Level 1A Target: Novice Low - Novice Mid

DOMAINS	NOVICE LOW	NOVICE MID	NOVICE HIGH
What language/ words do I use? *Vocabulary in context*	I can use a very limited number of familiar words that are repetitive.	I can use a limited number of memorized words and phrases in a familiar context.	I can use words and expressions that I have practiced on familiar topics.
How do I use language? *Function and Text Type*	I can copy familiar words, phrases, or incomplete sentences to complete lists, forms, charts, or organizers.	I can write lists, memorized phrases, supply information in a form, chart, or organizer on familiar topics	I can use learned vocabulary and structures to create simple sentences and questions to write short messages and notes with simple details on very familiar topics.
How well am I understood ? *Comprehensibility*	I am understood only with great effort by someone accustomed to a language learner.	I am somewhat understood by someone accustomed to a language learner.	I am often understood by someone accustomed to a language learner.
How well do I use the language? *Language Control*	I can use a very limited number of isolated words that are repetitive.	I am beginning to use basic structures with frequent errors.	I can use basic structures in present time with some errors and some memorized new structures in other time frames.
How well do I complete the task? *Ideas and Organization*	I can minimally complete the task with familiar content in writing.	I can complete the task with familiar content. My ideas are minimally developed and lack organization.	I can complete the task with familiar content and include some examples. My ideas are somewhat developed and organized.
How intercultural am I? *Interculturality* *Based on classroom tasks/ activities/ intercultural reflections and outside classroom experiences.*	I can apply my knowledge of cultural products, practices, and perspectives in order to convey respect and understanding in writing.	I can apply my knowledge of cultural products, practices, and perspectives in order to convey respect and understanding in writing.	I can apply my knowledge of cultural products, practices, and perspectives in order to convey respect and understanding in writing.

Adapted from Jefferson County Public Schools World Languages: Performance Assessment Rubrics (Kentucky), Howard County Public Schools World Languages (Maryland).

Level 1A *EntreCultures* Holistic Rubric

Interpretive Reading, Listening, and Viewing: Written, Print, Audio, Visual, and Audiovisual Resources

Level 1A Target: Novice Low - Novice Mid

Daily work, formative assessments

| 1 This is still a goal. |
| 2 Can do this with help. |
| 3 Can do this independently.[1] |

	INTERPRETIVE: Reading, Listening, and Viewing	1	2	3
NL	• Recognizes and understands a few memorized words and phrases in text or speech in familiar contexts. • Makes minimal inferences from visual and/or contextual clues and cognates. • Recognizes a few cultural products, practices, or perspectives related to daily life, including cultural behaviors and expressions.			
NM	• Recognizes and understands memorized words, phrases, and basic information in text or speech in familiar contexts. • Makes limited inferences from visual and/or contextual clues and cognates or may use other interpretive strategies. • Identifies a few cultural products, practices, or perspectives related to daily life, including cultural behaviors and expressions.*			
NH	• Understands and identifies words, phrases, questions, simple sentences, and sometimes the main idea in short pieces of informational text or speech in familiar contexts. • Makes a few inferences from visual and/or contextual clues, cognates and keywords or uses other interpretive strategies. • Identifies some cultural products, practices, and perspectives related to daily life, including cultural behaviors and expressions.*			

Based on classroom tasks/activities/ intercultural reflections and outside classroom experiences.

1 LinguaFolio®, NCSSFL. (2014). Interculturality. Retrieved from http://ncssfl.org/secure/index.php?interculturality, March 6, 2016.
* Novice range: using appropriate gestures, imitating appropriate etiquette, simple interactions in stores and restaurants.
** Intermediate range: demonstrating how to be culturally respectful, forms of address, appropriate interactions in everyday life.

LEARNER SELF-REFLECTION:
What interpretive strategies can I use to help me understand what I read/heard/viewed?

READING/VIEWING

❏ I preview titles, photos, layout, visuals, etc.

❏ I skim the text for cognates, familiar words, and phrases.

❏ I scan the text for specific details.

❏ I make predictions.

LISTENING/VIEWING

❏ I listen/watch for emotional reactions.

❏ I listen for time/time frame.

❏ I listen for tones and intonation .

❏ I listen for cognates, familiar words, phrases, and word-order patterns.

Adapted from Jefferson County Public Schools World Languages: Performance Assessment Rubrics (Kentucky).

Level 1A *EntreCultures* Holistic Rubric

Interpersonal Communication: Speaking, Listening, and Writing

Level 1A Target: Novice Low - Novice Mid

Daily class work, participation, class discussions, pair work, group work, and formative assessments

1	This is still a goal.
2	Can do this with help.
3	Can do this independently.[1]

	INTERPERSONAL COMMUNICATION: Speaking, Listening, and Writing	1	2	3
NL	• Communicates with a few memorized words and expressions in familiar contexts, but needs continual repetition to understand. Frequent interference from first language. • Speaks with frequent hesitation, pauses, and/or repetition. • Makes minimal inferences from visual and/or contextual clues, cognates. • Applies knowledge of cultural products, practices, and perspectives in order to interact with respect and understanding.*			
NM	• Communicates with some memorized words and expressions in familiar contexts, but needs continual repetition. Some interference from first language. • Maintains limited simple conversations with frequent hesitation, pauses, and/or repetition. • Makes limited inferences from visual and/or contextual clues, cognates. • Applies knowledge of cultural products, practices, and perspectives in order to interact with respect and understanding.*			
NH	• Communicates and exchanges information with learned words, phrases, simple sentences, and sometimes the main idea/simple details in familiar contexts. Some interference from first language. • Participates in short social interactions by asking and answering simple questions with hesitation, pauses, and/or repetition, using a few communication strategies. • Makes a few inferences from visual and/or contextual clues, cognates, or other language features. • Applies knowledge of cultural products, practices, and perspectives in order to interact with respect and understanding.*			

Based on classroom tasks/activities/ intercultural reflections and outside classroom experiences.

1 LinguaFolio®, NCSSFL. (2014). Interculturality. Retrieved from http://ncssfl.org/secure/index.php?interculturality, March 6, 2016.
* Novice range: using appropriate gestures, imitating appropriate etiquette, simple interactions in stores and restaurants.
** Intermediate range: demonstrating how to be culturally respectful, forms of address, appropriate interactions in everyday life.

LEARNER SELF-REFLECTION:
What communication strategies can I use to help me understand and make myself understood?

SPEAKING/WRITING

❑ I repeat words and phrases.

❑ I use facial expressions, gestures, and appropriate openings and closings.

❑ I self-correct when I am not understood.

❑ I imitate modeled words.

❑ I restate and rephrase using different words.

❑ I build upon what I've heard/read and elaborate in my response.

❑ I use level-appropriate vocabulary in familiar contexts.

LISTENING

❑ I ask for clarification or repetition.

❑ I repeat statements as questions for clarification.

❑ I listen for intonation.

❑ I listen for cognates, familiar words, phrases, and word-order patterns.

❑ I indicate lack of understanding.

❑ I ask questions.

Adapted from Jefferson County Public Schools World Languages: Performance Assessment Rubrics (Kentucky).

Level 1A *EntreCultures* **Holistic Rubric**

Presentational Speaking

Level 1A Target: Novice Low - Novice Mid

Daily class work, participation, share out or present to class, present to a group, formative assessments, and using Explorer audio and video recording feature

1	This is still a goal.
2	Can do this with help.
3	Can do this independently.[1]

	PRESENTATIONAL SPEAKING	1	2	3
NL	• Uses a few memorized words and expressions in familiar contexts. Frequent interference from first language. • Delivers message with great difficulty, using isolated words as structures. Speaks with frequent hesitation, pauses, and/or repetition. • Makes minimal use of gestures, self-correction, and examples/visuals to support the message. • Applies knowledge of cultural products, practices, and perspectives in order to interact with respect and understanding.*			
NM	• Uses some memorized words and expressions in familiar contexts. Some interference from first language. • Delivers message using some highly practiced basic structures with frequent errors. Speaks with frequent hesitation, pauses, and/or repetition. • Makes limited use of gestures, self-correction, and examples/visuals to support the message. • Applies knowledge of cultural products, practices, and perspectives in order to interact with respect and understanding.*			
NH	• Uses most highly practiced/learned words, phrases, and simple sentences in familiar contexts. Some interference from first language. • Delivers message using present time frame with some errors and some memorized new structures. Speaks with hesitation, pauses, and/or repetition. • Makes some use of gestures, self-correction, and examples/visuals to support the message, or a few other communication strategies. • Applies knowledge of cultural products, practices, and perspectives in order to interact with respect and understanding.*			

Based on classroom tasks/activities/ intercultural reflections and outside classroom experiences.

1 LinguaFolio®, NCSSFL. (2014). Interculturality. Retrieved from http://ncssfl.org/secure/index.php?interculturality, March 6, 2016.
* Novice range: using appropriate gestures, imitating appropriate etiquette, simple interactions in stores and restaurants.
** Intermediate range: demonstrating how to be culturally respectful, forms of address, appropriate interactions in everyday life.

LEARNER SELF-REFLECTION:
What communication strategies did I use to make myself understood to my audience?

PRESENTATIONAL SPEAKING

- ❏ I organize my presentation in a clear manner.
- ❏ I use facial expressions and gestures.
- ❏ I self-correct when I make mistakes.
- ❏ I present my own ideas.
- ❏ I use examples to support my message.
- ❏ I use visuals to support meaning.

- ❏ I include a hook to gain the audience's attention.
- ❏ I notice the reaction of the audience during the presentation.
- ❏ I repeat or rephrase if the audience doesn't understand.
- ❏ I project my voice so the audience can hear me.
- ❏ I practice my presentation before I present to the audience.

Adapted from Jefferson County Public Schools World Languages: Performance Assessment Rubrics (Kentucky).

Level 1A *EntreCultures* Holistic Rubric

Presentational Writing

Level 1A Target: Novice Low - Novice Mid

Daily written class work, forms, organizers, charts, messages, notes, formative assessments, and using Explorer quizzes, surveys, discussion forums, and more

1	This is still a goal.
2	Can do this with help.
3	Can do this independently.[1]

	PRESENTATIONAL WRITING	1	2	3
NL	• Uses a few memorized words and expressions in familiar contexts. Considerable interference from first language. • Completes the task minimally, using isolated words as structures. • Makes minimal use of presentational writing strategies. • Applies knowledge of cultural products, practices, and perspectives in order to convey respect and understanding in writing.*			
NM	• Uses some memorized words, expressions, and short sentences in familiar contexts. Frequent interference from first language. • Completes the task with some highly practiced basic structures with frequent errors. Ideas lack development and organization. • Makes limited use of presentational writing strategies. • Applies knowledge of cultural products, practices, and perspectives in order to convey respect and understanding in writing.*			
NH	• Uses most highly practiced words, phrases, questions, and simple sentences to write short, simple messages with simple details in familiar contexts. Some interference from first language. • Completes the tasks using present time frame and some memorized new structures. Ideas are partially developed and somewhat organized. • Makes some use of drafting, outlining, peer review, or other presentational writing strategies. • Applies knowledge of cultural products, practices, and perspectives in order to convey respect and understanding in writing.*			

Based on classroom tasks/activities/ intercultural reflections and outside classroom experiences.

1 LinguaFolio®, NCSSFL. (2014). Interculturality. Retrieved from http://ncssfl.org/secure/index.php?interculturality, March 6, 2016.
* Novice range: using appropriate gestures, imitating appropriate etiquette, simple interactions in stores and restaurants.
** Intermediate range: demonstrating how to be culturally respectful, forms of address, appropriate interactions in everyday life.

LEARNER SELF-REFLECTION:

What communication strategies can I use to make my message understood to the reader?

PRESENTATIONAL WRITING

❏ I organize my presentation in a clear manner.

❏ I include a hook to gain the reader's attention.

❏ I present my own ideas.

❏ I write an outline before I begin to write.

❏ I cite my sources if I have done research on the topic.

❏ I write a draft of my message.

❏ I use examples to support my message.

❏ I ask someone to peer edit my draft before I submit it.

❏ I check all spelling and grammar before I submit it.

❏ I make sure my writing is clear and my handwriting is legible.

Adapted from Jefferson County Public Schools World Languages: Performance Assessment Rubrics (Kentucky).

Rubrics

EntreCultures 1A – General *J'avance* Rubric

DOMAINS	BEGINNING	DEVELOPING	MEETING
Task Completion	Minimal completion of the task.	Partial completion of the task.	Adequate completion of the task.
	Ideas are not developed.	Ideas are minimally developed.	Ideas are appropriately developed.
	Responses display minimal/no understanding of the information presented.	Responses display a limited understanding of the information presented.	Responses display an adequate understanding of the information presented.
Structures (Grammar) in Context	Minimal use of target language structures.	Limited accuracy with target language structures.	Generally accurate use of target language structures with a few errors.
	Errors make comprehension difficult.	Errors may impede comprehension.	Errors do not impede comprehension.
Vocabulary in Context	Vocabulary used is inaccurate and repetitive and minimally includes essential unit vocabulary.	Vocabulary is limited to highly practiced words and expressions and includes some essential unit vocabulary.	Vocabulary is adequate and mostly relevant to the task and includes essential unit vocabulary.
Comprehensibility & Pronunciation	Message may be comprehensible with great difficulty.	Message is somewhat comprehensible.	Message is generally comprehensible.
	Pronunciation impedes ability to understand.	Pronunciation may interfere with ability to understand.	Pronunciation facilitates understanding.
Quality of Interaction or Presentation	Insufficient language to communicate message; reverts to English.	Limited language to communicate message and may revert to English.	Attempts creative use of language to communicate message.
	Requires prompting or teacher assistance to maintain interaction/presentation.	Requires some prompting or teacher assistance to maintain interaction/presentation.	May require prompting or teacher assistance to maintain interaction/presentation.
	Frequent hesitations.	Some hesitations.	Occasional hesitations.

Not all domains will apply to every mode. There is also a single-point rubric available in Explorer for each *J'avance* assessment.

	Scores:		
EXCEEDING	**INTERPRETIVE**	**INTERPERSONAL**	**PRESENTATIONAL**
Exceeds task expectations.			
Ideas are well developed.			
Responses display a complete understanding of the information presented, including details.			
Very accurate use of target language structures with minimal errors.			
Errors do not impede comprehension.			
Vocabulary is varied and relevant to the task and may exceed essential unit vocabulary.			
Message is fully comprehensible.			
Pronunciation enhances understanding.			
Creative use of language to communicate message.			
Little to no prompting needed to maintain interaction/presentation.			
Few to no hesitations.			

Rubrics

Integrated Performance Assessment Rubric

Unité préliminaire – *Les colonies de vacances*

Domains	Task Components
INTERPRETIVE ASSESSMENT **Interpretive Print** *Étape 1*	**Recognizes key words** Student records the cognates he/she recognizes in an advertisement for summer camps.
Interpretive Print *Étape 2*	**Identifies information** Student selects the camp he/she wants to attend by completing the required information on the graphic organizer as evidence of comprehension.
Interpretive Listening *Étape 3*	**Understands familiar words and phrases** Student listens to three campers introduce themselves and completes the chart with the campers' personal information (name, origin, age, and birthday).
INTERPERSONAL ASSESSMENT **Interpersonal Speaking**	**Asks and answers questions** Student participates in a short conversation with one camper. The student greets and introduces self, providing name, age, birthday, and a goodbye.

Novice Low	Novice Mid	Novice High
Recognizes a **few** of the cognates related to the topic.	Recognizes **some** of the cognates related to the topic.	Recognizes **most** of the cognates related to the topic.
Identifies a **few** items of the required information.	Identifies **some** of the required information.	Identifies **most** of the required information.
Identifies **limited** information for each camper.	Accurately identifies **some** information for each camper.	Accurately identifies **most** of the information for each camper.
Conversation includes a **few** of the task's components using memorized words and phrases.	Conversation includes **some** of the task's components using some familiar and memorized words, phrases, questions, and attempts simple sentences.	Conversation includes **most** of the task's components using familiar and memorized words, phrases, questions, and simple sentences.
The conversation is understood only with **great effort**.	The conversation is **somewhat** understood despite frequent errors.	The conversation is **often** understood despite errors.

Rubrics

Integrated Performance Assessment Rubric

Unité 1 – *Un échange scolaire*

Domains	Task Components
INTERPRETIVE ASSESSMENT **Interpretive Audiovisual** *Étape 1*	**Recognizes key words** Student checks the key words heard in student video blogs; compares with a classmate's key words.
Interpretive Audiovisual *Étape 2*	**Identifies information** Student completes missing information on the bloggers' enrollment forms.
Interpretive Reading and Audiovisual *Étape 3*	**Infers details** Student identifies key characteristics of each blogger on a checklist.
INTERPERSONAL ASSESSMENT **Interpersonal Writing**	**Responds in an email** Student writes an email to exchange student of choice by addressing their video blog. Greets and introduces self, providing name, age, personal details, and similarities with exchange student. Student asks two questions about likes and dislikes, gives thanks for video blog, and closes email appropriately.
PRESENTATIONAL ASSESSMENT **Presentational Speaking** *Étape 1*	**Creates video blog** Student prepares video blog to share with host family; includes greeting, name, age, origin, languages, two likes, and closing.
Presentational Writing *Étape 2*	**Compares similarities** Student completes two sentences regarding two similarities with the bloggers.

Novice Low	Novice Mid	Novice High
Recognizes a **few** of the familiar words and phrases related to the topic.	Recognizes **some** of the words, familiar phrases, and some simple sentences related to the topic.	Recognizes **most** of the words, phrases, and simple sentences related to the topic.
Identifies a **few** items from the missing information.	Identifies **some** of the missing information.	Identifies **most** of the missing information.
Identifies and infers a **few** details of each blogger.	Identifies and infers **some** of the details of each blogger.	Identifies and infers **most** of the details of each blogger.
Message includes a **few** of the task's components using memorized words and phrases. The message is understood only with **great effort**.	Message includes **some** of the task's components using some familiar words, memorized phrases, and attempts at simple questions and simple sentences. The message is **somewhat** understood despite frequent errors.	Message includes **most** of the task's components using familiar words, phrases, questions, and simple sentences. The message is **often** understood despite errors.
The video blog includes a **few** of the task's components using a few familiar words and memorized phrases. The delivery includes **frequent** hesitation, pauses, and repetition and is understood with **great effort** by someone accustomed to a language learner.	The video blog includes **some** of the task's components using familiar words, memorized phrases, and attempts at a few simple sentences. The delivery includes hesitation, pauses, and/or repetition and is **somewhat** understood by someone accustomed to a language learner.	The video blog includes **most** of the task's components using familiar words, phrases, and some simple sentences. The delivery includes **some** hesitation, pauses, and/or repetition and is **mostly** understood by someone accustomed to a language learner.
Interculturality Makes **limited** cultural comparisons.	**Interculturality** Makes **somewhat** relevant cultural comparisons.	**Interculturality** Makes **mostly** relevant cultural comparisons.

Rubrics

Integrated Performance Assessment Rubric

Unité 2 – *Un échange virtuel*

Domains	Task Components
INTERPRETIVE ASSESSMENT **Interpretive Print** *Étape 1*	**Recognizes key words** Student completes a graphic organizer to identify classes and/or activities that take place in different locations based on the information included in the provided schedule.
Interpretive Print *Étape 2*	**Compares cultural information** Using the information from Sofia's schedule and the graphic organizer, the student writes one similarity and one difference between class schedules in Algeria and in his or her community.
INTERPERSONAL ASSESSMENT **Interpersonal Speaking**	**Asks and answers questions** Student exchanges information with Sofia by responding to and asking questions.
PRESENTATIONAL ASSESSMENT **Presentational Speaking**	**Presents a school day** Student prepares and creates a video or visual presentation about a day at his or her school including: starting and ending times, school supplies, classes and times of day, class preferences, and after school activities.

Novice Low	Novice Mid	Novice High
Identifies **limited** required information.	Identifies **some** of the required information.	Identifies **most** of the required information.
Interculturality Identifies **minimal** information and may not make a comparison between the two cultures.	**Interculturality** Identifies a **somewhat** relevant similarity and difference between the two cultures.	**Interculturality** Identifies a **mostly** relevant similarity and difference between the two cultures.
Responds to a **few** questions in the task using memorized and familiar words and phrases. Student is understood only with **great effort**.	Responds to and asks **some** of the questions in the task using familiar and memorized words, phrases, questions, and attempts simple sentences. Student is **somewhat** understood despite frequent errors.	Responds to and asks **most** of the questions in the task using familiar and memorized words, phrases, questions, and simple sentences. Student is **often** understood despite errors.
The presentation includes a **few** of the task's components using memorized and familiar words and phrases. The delivery includes **continuous** hesitation, pauses, repetition, and the message is understood only with **great effort**.	The presentation includes **some** of the task's components using familiar words, phrases, and attempts at a few simple sentences. The delivery includes **frequent** hesitation, pauses, and/or repetition, and the message is **somewhat** understood despite frequent errors.	The presentation includes **most** of the task's components using familiar words, phrases, and some simple sentences. The delivery includes **some** hesitation, pauses, and/or repetition, and the message is **often** understood despite errors.

Rubrics

Integrated Performance Assessment Rubric

Unité 3 – *Une nouvelle famille, une nouvelle culture*

Domains	Task Components
INTERPRETIVE ASSESSMENT **Interpretive Video**	**Recognizes keywords/components** Student completes a chart to identify attributes of three bloggers based on the information in their three videos.
INTERPERSONAL ASSESSMENT **Interpersonal Speaking**	**Asks and answers questions** Student prepares to exchange information with one of the bloggers by responding to and asking questions about his or her family with a partner.
PRESENTATIONAL ASSESSMENT **Presentational Writing**	**Creates a digital album** Student prepares and creates a digital album about a minimum of three family members, using pictures and written descriptions including: name, age, relationship to them and to others, adjectives describing physical appearance and personality, activities and likes and dislikes.

Novice Low	Novice Mid	Novice High
Identifies **limited** required information.	Identifies **some** of the required information.	Identifies **most** of the required information.
Interculturality Minimally identifies personal similarities and differences with a Francophone teenager.	**Interculturality** Somewhat identifies personal similarities and differences with a Francophone teenager.	**Interculturality** Adequately identifies personal similarities and differences with a Francophone teenager.
Responds to a **few** questions in the task using memorized and familiar words and phrases.	Responds to and asks **some** of the questions in the task using familiar and memorized words, phrases, questions, and attempts simple sentences.	Responds to and asks **most** of the questions in the task using familiar and memorized words, phrases, questions, and simple sentences.
Student is understood only with **great effort**.	Student is **somewhat** understood despite frequent errors.	Student is **often** understood despite errors.
The presentation includes a **few** of the task's components using memorized and familiar words and phrases.	The presentation includes **some** of the task's components using familiar words, phrases, and attempts at a few simple sentences.	The presentation includes **most** of the task's components using familiar words, phrases, and some simple sentences.
The descriptions include **continuous** repetition and mistakes. The message is understood only with **great effort**.	The descriptions include **frequent** repetition and mistakes. The message is **somewhat** understood despite frequent errors.	The descriptions include **some** repetition and mistakes. The message is **often** understood despite errors.

EntreCultures 1A
AP® and IB Correlation Guide

AP® Theme	Unit 0	Unit 1	Unit 2	Unit 3
1. Les défis mondiaux				
Contexte 1: L'économie				
Contexte 2: L'environnement				
Contexte 3: L'alimentation et la santé				
Contexte 4: La tolérance				
Contexte 5: Les droits de l'être humain				
Contexte 6: La paix et la guerre				
2. La Science et la Technologie				
Contexte 1: La technologie et ses effets sur la société			✔	
Contexte 2: Les découvertes et les inventions	✔			
Contexte 3: Les choix moraux				
Contexte 4: La propriété intellectuelle				
Contexte 5: La recherche et ses nouvelle frontières				
Contexte 6: L'avenir de la technologie			✔	
3. La Vie Contemporaine				
Contexte 1: L'éducation et le monde du travail	✔	✔	✔	
Contexte 2: Les loisirs et le sport	✔	✔		✔
Contexte 3: Les voyages	✔	✔		✔
Contexte 4: La publicité et le marketing	✔	✔		✔
Contexte 5: Le logement		✔		✔
Contexte 6: Les fêtes et les rites de passage	✔			
4. La Quête de Soi				
Contexte 1: L'aliénation et l'assimilation				
Contexte 2: L'identité linguistique	✔	✔		
Contexte 3: Le nationalisme et le patriotisme				
Contexte 4: Le pluriculturalisme	✔	✔	✔	✔
Contexte 5: Les croyances et les systèmes de valeurs				
Contexte 6: La sexualité				

AP® Theme	Unit 0	Unit 1	Unit 2	Unit 3
5. La Famille et la Communauté				
Contexte 1: L'enfance et l'adolescence				
Contexte 2: L'amitié et l'amour				✔
Contexte 3: Les rapports sociaux	✔	✔		✔
Contexte 4: Les coutumes	✔		✔	✔
Contexte 5: La citoyenneté				
Contexte 6: La famille				✔
6. L'Esthétique				
Contexte 1: Le beau				
Contexte 2: Le patrimoine	✔	✔		
Contexte 3: Les arts littéraires				✔
Contexte 4: Les arts visuels				
Contexte 5: L'architecture	✔			
Contexte 6: La musique et l'art du spectacle		✔		

IB Theme	Unit 0	Unit 1	Unit 2	Unit 3
1. Identités	✔	✔	✔	✔
2. Expériences	✔	✔	✔	✔
3. Ingéniosité humaine	✔	✔	✔	✔
4. Organisation sociale	✔	✔	✔	✔
5. Partage de la planète				

Glossary French-English

actif/active active (1, 3)

l' **activité (f.)** activity (2)

âgé/âgée old (3)

l' **agenda (m.)** scolaire school planner (2)

aider to help (2)

l' **algèbre (f.)** algebra (2)

l' **allemand (m.)** the German language (1)

allemand/allemande German (1)

aller au café/cinéma to go to a café/cinema (1)

ambitieux/ambitieuse ambitious (1, 3)

américain/américaine American (1, 3)

amusant/amusante funny (2, 3)

l' **anglais (m.)** the English language (1, 2)

anglais/anglaise English (1)

août August (0)

l' **appartement (m.)** apartment (3)

À quelle heure? At what time? (2)

l' **arabe (m.)** the Arabic language (1, 2)

arabe (inv.) Arabic (1, 2)

l' **artiste (inv.)** artist (1)

les **arts (m. pl.) visuels** visual arts (2)

asseyez-vous sit down (0)

assez rather (3)

l' **athlète (inv.)** athlete (1)

au revoir goodbye (0)

avoir une interrogation (interro) to take a test (2)

avril April (0)

le **balcon** balcony (3)

beau/belle beautiful (3)

bénévole volunteer (1)

bilingue bilingual (1, 3)

la **biologie** biology (2)

le **blogueur/la blogueuse** blogger (1)

blond/blonde blond (3)

bonjour hello (0)

brun/brune brunette (3)

le **bureau** desk, office (2, 3)

le **cahier** notebook (2)

la **calculatrice** calculator (2)

la **campagne** countryside (3)

canadien/canadienne Canadian (1, 3)

la **cantine** cafeteria (2)

le **casier** locker (2)

Ça va très bien, merci. I'm very well, thanks. (0)

Ça va bien. Et toi? I'm fine. And you? (0)

cent (one) hundred (3)

C'est quand ton anniversaire? When is your birthday? (0, 1)

la **chaise** chair (2, 3)

la **chambre à coucher** bedroom (3)

chanter to sing (1, 2)

le **chanteur/la chanteuse** singer (1)

le **chinois** the Chinese language (1)

chinois/chinoise Chinese (1)

la **chorale** chorus (2)

ciao ciao (0)

cinq five (0)

cinquante fifty (2)

cinquante-sept fifty-seven (2)

les ciseaux (m. pl.) scissors (2)

le classeur binder (2)

le collège middle school (2)

comme ci, comme ça so-so, okay (0)

Comment? How? (1)

Comment allez-vous (formal) How are you? (0)

Comment ça va? (informal) How are you? (0, 1)

Comment t'appelles-tu? What's your name? (0, 1)

la conversation conversation (0)

la cour courtyard (2)

courageux/courageuse courageous (1, 3)

le cours class, course (2)

le cours commence à... The class begins at... (2)

le cours termine à... The class ends at... (2)

le/la cousin/cousine cousin (3)

le crayon pencil (2)

le créateur/la créatrice de mode designer (1)

créatif/créative creative (3)

le créole the Créole language (1)

créole (inv.) Créole (1)

la cuisine kitchen (3)

le/la cycliste (inv.) cyclist (1)

danser to dance (1, 2)

le danseur/la danseuse dancer (1)

la date date (0)

décembre December (0)

déjeuner to eat lunch (2)

le déjeuner lunch (2)

dessiner to draw (1, 2)

deux two (0)

le dictionnaire dictionary (2)

difficile difficult (2)

dimanche Sunday (0)

discuter to discuss (1, 2)

dix ten (0)

dix-sept seventeen (0)

dix-huit eighteen (0)

dix-neuf nineteen (0)

dormir to sleep (1)

D'où viens-tu? Where do you come from? (0, 1)

douze twelve (0)

l' école (f.) school (2)

écouter de la musique to listen to music (1)

écoutez listen (0)

écrire to write (1)

l' éducation (f.) physique et sportive physical education (2)

l' élève (inv.) student (1)

l' enfant (m. or f.) child (3)

enseigner to teach (2)

l' espagnol (m.) the Spanish language (1, 2)

espagnol/espagnole Spanish (1)

Est-ce que tu es élève? Are you a student? (1)

étudier to study (1, 2)

l' explorateur (m.)/l'exploratrice (f.) explorer (1)

facile easy (2)

faire attention to pay attention (2)

fascinant/fascinante fascinating (2)

fatigant/fatigante tiring (2)

fermez vos livres close your books (0)

la feuille de papier sheet of paper (2)

le feutre marker (2)

février February (0)

la fille daughter (3)

le fils son (3)

finir to finish (2)

le fourniture scolaire school supply (2)

le français the French language (0, 1, 2)

français/française French (0, 1, 3)

le frère brother (3)

le garage garage (3)

généreux/généreuse generous (1, 3)

génial/géniale awesome (2)

gentil/gentille nice, kind (3)

la géographie (géo) geography (2)

grand/grande tall (3)

la grand-mère grandmother (3)

le grand-père grandfather (3)

les grands-parents (m. pl.) grandparents (3)

gros/grosse fat, big (3)

le gymnase gymnasium (2)

habiter to live (1)

l' heure (f.) time, hour (2)

l' histoire (f.) history (2)

huit eight (0)

il vous faut... you need... (0)

l' immeuble (m.) apartment building (3)

l' informatique (f.) technology (2)

inspirant/inspirante inspiring (2)

intelligent/intelligente smart, intelligent (3)

intéressant/intéressante interesting (2)

l' inventeur (m.)/l'inventrice (f.) inventor (1)

l' italien (m.) the Italian language (1)

italien/italienne Italian (1)

janvier January (0)

le jardin garden (3)

jeudi Thursday (0)

jeune young (3)

Je m'appelle... My name is... (0)

Je viens de... I'm from... (0)

jouer au sport to play a sport (1)

jouer aux jeux vidéo to play video games (1)

jouer de la musique to play music (1)

le jour day (0)

juillet July (0)

juin June (0)

le laboratoire (labo) laboratory (2)

les langues (f. pl.) vivantes modern languages (2)

le latin Latin (2)

levez la main raise your hand (0)

levez-vous stand up (0)

le lieu place (2)

lire to read (1)

la littérature literature (2)

le livre book (2)

lundi Monday (0)

le lycée high school (2)

mai May (0)

la maison house (3)

mal bad, not well at all (0)

manger (g → ge) to eat (1, 2)

mardi Tuesday (0)

mars March (0)

les mathétiques (f. pl.) (maths) mathematics (2)

les matières (f. pl.) school subjects (2)

méchant/méchante mean (3)

la médiathèque media center (2)

les membres (m. pl.) de la famille family members (3)

la mère mother (3)

mes activités préférées my preferred activities (1)

mignon/mignonne cute (3)

le mois month (0)

Mon anniversaire est le... My birthday is... (0)

les mots interrogatifs question words (1)

le musicien/la musicienne musician (1)

la musique music (2)

le néerlandais the Dutch language (1)

néerlandais/néerlandaise Dutch (1)

neuf nine (0)

novembre November (0)

le **numéro** number (0)

les **numéros (m. pl.) de 30 à 69** the numbers from 30 to 69 (2)

octobre October (0)

l' **oncle** uncle (3)

onze eleven (0)

l' **orchestra (m.)** orchestra (2)

l' **ordinateur (m.)** computer (2)

organiser to organize (2)

Où?/D'où? Where?/From where? (1)

ouvrez vos livres open your books (0)

parce que/qu' because (2)

les **parents (m. pl.)** parents (3)

parler to speak (2)

parlez avec votre voisin talk with your neighbor (0)

parlez en français speak in French (0)

participer aux clubs to participate in clubs (2)

pas mal not bad (0)

passer du temps avec des amis to spend time with friends (1)

patient/patiente patient (3)

peindre to paint (1)

le **père** father (3)

la **personne** person (2)

les **personnes (f. pl.)** people (2)

petit/petite small/short (3)

le/la **photographe (inv.)** photographer (1)

la **physique** physics (2)

le/la **poète (inv.)** poet (1)

le **polonais** the Polish language (1)

polonais/polonaise Polish (1)

le **portable** cell phone (2)

le **portugais** the Portuguese language (1)

portugais/portugaise Portuguese (1)

Pourquoi? Why? (1)

Pourquoi est-ce que tu étudies le français? Why do you study French? (1)

le **premier** the first (day of the month) (0)

les **premières conversations** first conversations (0)

le **principal/la principale** principal (2)

le/la **professeur** teacher (2)

la **psychologie** psychology (2)

Quand? When? (1)

quarante forty (2)

quarante-quatre forty-four (2)

quatorze fourteen (0)

quatre four (0)

quatre-vingts eighty (3)

quatre-vingt-un eighty-one (3)

quatre-vingt-deux eighty-two (3)

quatre-vingt-dix ninety (3)

quatre-vingt-onze ninety-one (3)

quatre-vingt-douze ninety-two (3)

québécois/québécoise from Quebec (1, 3)

Quel âge as-tu? How old are you? (1)

Quel(le)? Which? What? (1)

Quelle est la date? What is the date? (0, 1)

Quelle heure est-il? What time is it? (2)

Quelles langues est-ce que parles? Which languages do you speak? (1)

Que/qu'? What? (1)

Qu'est-ce que tu aimes étudier? What do you like to study? (1)

Qui? Who? (1)

Qui est ton professeur? Who is your teacher? (1)

Qui suis-je? Who am I? (1)

quinze fifteen (0)

rarement rarely (3)

la **récréation (récré)** recess/break (2)

regarder une série/un film to watch a show/film (1)

regardez-moi look at me (0)

répétez repeat (0)

répondre to respond/answer (2)

retournez à vos places return to your seats (0)

roux/rousse red-headed (3)

le sac à dos backpack (2)

la salle à manger dining room (3)

la salle de bains bathroom (3)

la salle de classe classroom (0, 2)

le salon living room (3)

salut hi (0)

samedi Saturday (0)

les sciences (f. pl.) de la vie et de la terre (SVT) life and earth science (2)

les sciences (f. pl.) sociales social sciences (2)

le/la scientifique (inv.) scientist (1)

seize sixteen (0)

la semaine week (2)

sept seven (0)

septembre Septembre (0)

sérieux/sérieuse serious (1)

si so (3)

s'il vous plaît please (0)

six six (0)

la sœur sister (3)

soixante sixty (2)

soixante-dix seventy (3)

soixante-douze seventy-two (3)

soixante-neuf sixty-nine (2)

soixante-onze seventy-one (3)

soixante-treize seventy-three (3)

souvent often (3)

le sport physical education (2)

sportif/sportive athletic (1)

strict/stricte strict, firm (3)

le stylo pen (2)

surfer sur internet to surf the Internet/web (1)

le tableau whiteboard/chalkboard (2)

la tablette tablet (2)

le taille crayon pencil sharpener (2)

la tante aunt (3)

les toilettes (f. pl.) WC, toilets (3)

toujours always (3)

travailler to work (1)

travailler au bureau to work in the office (2)

travailler en équipe to work in teams (2)

treize thirteen (0)

trente thirty (0, 2)

trente et un thirty-one (0, 2)

trois three (0)

trop too (3)

la trousse pencil case (2)

un one (0)

utiliser to use (2)

végétarien/végétarienne vegetarian (1)

vendredi Friday (0)

le vietnamien the Vietnamese language (1)

vietnamien/vietnamienne Vietnamese (1)

la ville city (3)

vingt twenty (0)

vingt-deux twenty-two (0)

vingt-cinq twenty-five (0)

vingt et un twenty-one (0)

vingt-huit twenty-eight (0)

vingt-neuf twenty-nine (0)

vingt-quatre twenty-four (0)

vingt-sept twenty-nine (0)

vingt-six twenty-six (0)

vingt-trois twenty-three (0)

voyager (g → ge) to travel (1)

vraiment really (3)

le week-end weekend (2)

Expressions utiles French-English

assez rather (3)

C'est génial! That's awesome! (3)

C'est intéressant! That's interesting! (1)

C'est le + numéro + mois It's month + number (0)

C'est super! That's great! (1)

D'accord! Ok! (3)

Il y a... There is/are... (2)

J'ai beaucoup de/d'... I have a lot of... (2)

J'ai besoin de/d'... I need... (2)

Je n'ai pas beaucoup de/d'... I do not have a lot of... (2)

Je n'ai pas besoin de/d'... I don't need... (2)

Je ne sais pas! I don't know! (3)

Je sais! I know! (3)

jouer à des jeux vidéo/jouer aux jeux vidéo to play video games (1)

Moi aussi! Me too! (1)

Moi non plus! Me neither! (1)

pendant la semaine during the week (2)

pendant le week-end during the weekend (2)

rarement rarely (3)

si so (3)

souvent often (3)

Très bien! Very good! (1)

trop too (3)

Vachement cool! Really cool! (3)

vraiment really (3)

Glossary English-French

active actif/active (1, 3)

activity l'activité (2)

algebra l'algèbre (f.) (2)

always toujours (3)

ambitious ambitieux/ambitieuse (1, 3)

American américain/américaine (1, 3)

apartment l'appartement (3)

apartment building l'immeuble (m.) (3)

April avril (0)

Arabic arabe (inv.) (1, 2)

the **Arabic language** l'arabe (m.) (1, 2)

Are you a student? Est-ce que tu es élève? (1)

artist l'artiste (inv.) (1)

At what time? À quelle heure? (2)

athlete l'athlète (inv.) (1)

athletic sportif/sportive (1)

to **answer** répondre (2)

August août (0)

aunt la tante (3)

awesome génial/géniale (2)

backpack le sac à dos (2)

bad, not well at all mal (0)

balcony le balcon (3)

bathroom la salle de bains (3)

beautiful beau/belle (3)

because parce que/qu' (2)

bedroom la chambre à coucher (3)

big gros/grosse (3)

bilingual bilingue (1, 3)

binder le classeur (2)

biology la biologie (2)

blackboard le tableau (2)

blond blond/blonde (3)

blogger le blogueur/la blogueuse (1)

book le livre (2)

break/recess la récréation (récré) (2)

brother le frère (3)

brunette brun/brune (3)

cafeteria la cantine (2)

calculator la calculatrice (2)

Canadian canadien/canadienne (1, 3)

cell phone le portable (2)

chair la chaise (2, 3)

the **Chinese language** le chinois (1)

Chinese chinois/chinoise (1)

child l'enfant (m. or f.) (3)

chorus la chorale (2)

ciao ciao (0)

city la ville (3)

class le cours (2)

the **class begins at...** le cours commence à... (2)

the **class ends at...** le cours termine à... (2)

classroom la salle de classe (0, 2)

close your books fermez vos livres (0)

computer l'ordinateur (2)

conversation la conversation (0)

countryside la campagne (3)

courageous courageux/courageuse (1, 3)

course le cours (2)

courtyard la cour (2)

cousin le/la cousin/cousine (3)

creative créative (3)

Créole créole (inv.) (1)

the **Créole language** le créole (1)

cute mignon/mignonne (3)

cyclist le/la cycliste (inv.) (1)

to **dance** danser (1, 2)

dancer le danseur/la danseuse (1)

daughter la fille (3)

date la date (0)

day le jour (0)

December décembre (0)

desk le bureau (2)

designer le créateur/la créatrice de mode (1)

difficult difficile (2)

dictionary le dictionnaire (2)

dining room la salle à manger (3)

to **discuss** discuter (1, 2)

to **draw** dessiner (1, 2)

Dutch néerlandais/néerlandaise (1)

the **Dutch language** le néerlandais (1)

easy facile (2)

to **eat** manger (g → ge) (1, 2)

to **eat lunch** déjeuner (2)

eight huit (0)

eighteen dix-huit (0)

eighty quatre-vingts (3)

eighty-one quatre-vingt-un (3)

eighty-two quatre-vingt-deux (3)

eleven onze (0)

English anglais/anglaise (1)

the **English language** l'anglais (m.) (1, 2)

explorer l'explorateur (m.)/l'exploratrice (f.) (1)

family members les membres (m. pl.) de la famille (3)

fascinating fascinant/fascinante (2)

fat gros/grosse (3)

father le père (3)

February février (0)

fifteen quinze (0)

fifty cinquante (2)

fifty-seven cinquante-sept (2)

to **finish** finir (2)

firm strict/stricte (3)

five cinq (0)

the **first (day of the month)** le premier (0)

forty quarante (2)

forty-four quarante-quatre (2)

four quatre (0)

fourteen quatorze (0)

French français/française (0, 1, 3)

the **French language** le français (0, 1, 2)

Friday vendredi (0)

funny amusant/amusante (2, 3)

garage le garage (3)

garden le jardin (3)

generous généreux/généreuse (1, 3)

geography la géographie (géo) (2)

German allemand/allemande (1)

the **German language** l'allemand (m.) (1)

to **go to a café/cinema** aller au café/cinéma (1)

goodbye au revoir (0)

grandfather le grand-père (3)

grandmother la grand-mère (3)

grandparents les grands-parents (m. pl.) (3)

gymnasium le gymnase (2)

hello bonjour (0)

to **help** aider (2)

hi salut (0)

high school le lycée (2)

history l'histoire (f.) (2)

hour l'heure (f.) (2)

house la maison (3)

How? Comment? (1)

How are you? Comment allez-vous? (formal) (0)

How are you? Comment ça va? (informal) (0, 1)

How old are you? Quel âge as-tu? (1)

hundred cent (3)

I'm fine. And you? Ça va bien. Et toi? (0)

I'm from... Je viens de... (0)

I'm very well, thanks. Ça va très bien, merci. (0)

inspiring inspirant/inspirante (2)

intelligent intelligent/intelligente (3)

interesting intéressant/intéressante (2)

inventor l'inventeur (m.)/l'inventrice (f.) (1)

Italian italien/italienne (1)

the Italian language l'italien (m.) (1)

January janvier (0)

July juillet (0)

June juin (0)

kind gentil/gentille (3)

kitchen la cuisine (3)

laboratory le laboratoire (labo) (2)

Latin le latin (2)

life and earth science les sciences (f. pl.) de la vie et de la terre (SVT) (2)

listen écoutez (0)

to listen to music écouter de la musique (1)

literature la littérature (2)

to live habiter (1)

living room le salon (3)

locker le caiser (2)

look at me regardez-moi (0)

lunch le déjeuner (2)

March mars (0)

marker le feutre (2)

mathematics les mathétiques (f. pl.) (maths) (2)

May mai (0)

mean méchant/méchante (3)

media center la médiathèque (2)

middle school le collège (2)

modern languages les langues (f. pl.) vivantes (2)

Monday lundi (0)

month le mois (0)

mother la mère (3)

music la musique (2)

musician le musicien/la musicienne (1)

My birthday is... Mon anniversaire est... (0)

My name is... Je m'appelle... (0)

my preferred activities mes activités préférées (1)

nice gentil/gentille (3)

nine neuf (0)

nineteen dix-neuf (0)

ninety quatre-vingt-dix (3)

ninety-one quatre-vingt-onze (3)

ninety-two quatre-vingt-douze (3)

not bad pas mal (0)

notebook le cahier (2)

November novembre (0)

number le numéro (0)

the numbers from 30 to 69 les numéros (m. pl.) de 30 à 69 (2)

October octobre (0)

office le bureau (2)

often souvent (3)

old âgé/âgée (3)

one un (0)

open your books ouvrez vos livres (0)

orchestra l'orchestra (2)

to organize organiser (2)

to paint peindre (1)

parents les parents (m. pl.) (3)

to participate in clubs participer aux clubs (2)

patient patient/patiente (3)

to pay attention faire attention (2)

pen le stylo (2)

pencil le crayon (2)

pencil case la trousse (2)

pencil sharpener le taille crayon (2)

people les personnes (f. pl.) (2)

person la personne (2)

photographer le/la photographe (inv.) (1)

physical education l'éducation (f.) physique et sportive, le sport (2)

physics la physique (2)

place le lieu (2)

to **play a sport** jouer au sport (1)

to **play music** jouer de la musique (1)

to **play video games** jouer à des jeux vidéo, jouer aux jeux vidéo (1)

please s'il vous plaît (0)

poet le/la poète (inv.) (1)

Polish polonais/polonaise (1)

the **Polish language** le polonais (1)

Portuguese portugais/portugaise (1)

the **Portuguese language** le portugais (1)

psychology la psychologie (2)

from **Quebec** québécois/québécoise (1, 3)

question words les mots interrogatifs (1)

raise your hand levez la main (0)

rarely rarement (3)

rather assez (3)

to **read** lire (1)

really vraiment (3)

recess/break la récréation (récré) (2)

red-headed roux/rousse (3)

repeat répétez (0)

to **respond** répondre (2)

return to your seats retournez à vos places (0)

Saturday samedi (0)

school l'école (f.) (2)

school planner l'agenda (m.) scolaire (2)

school subjects les matières (f. pl.) (2)

school supply le fourniture scolaire (2)

scientist le/la scientifique (inv.) (1)

scissors les ciseaux (m. pl.) (2)

September septembre (0)

serious sérieux/sérieuse (1)

seven sept (0)

seventeen dix-sept (0)

seventy soixante-dix (3)

seventy-one soixante-onze (3)

seventy-two soixante-douze (3)

seventy-three soixante-treize (3)

sheet of paper la feuille de papier (2)

short petit/petite (3)

to **sing** chanter (1, 3)

singer le chanteur/la chanteuse (1)

sister la sœur (3)

sit down asseyez-vous (0)

six six (0)

sixteen seize (0)

sixty soixante (2)

sixty-nine soixante-neuf (2)

to **sleep** dormir (1)

small petit/petite (3)

smart intelligent/intelligente (3)

so si (3)

social sciences les sciences (f. pl.) sociales (2)

son le fils (3)

so-so, okay comme ci, comme ça (0)

Spanish espagnol/espagnole (1)

the **Spanish language** l'espagnol (m.) (1, 2)

to **speak** parler (2)

speak in French parlez en français (0)

to **spend time with friends** passer du temps (1)

stand up levez-vous (0)

strict strict/stricte (3)

student l'élève (inv.) (1)

to study étudier (1, 2)

Sunday dimanche (0)

to surf the Internet/web surfer sur internet (1)

tablet la tablette (2)

to take a test avoir une interrogation (interro) (2)

talk with your neighbor parlez avec votre voisin (0)

tall grand/grande (3)

to teach enseigner (2)

teacher le/la professeur (2)

technology l'informatique (f.) (2)

ten dix (0)

thirteen treize (0)

thirty trente (0, 2)

thirty-one trente et un (0, 2)

three trois (0)

Thursday jeudi (0)

time l'heure (f.) (2)

tiring fatigant/fatigante (2)

toilets les toilettes (f. pl.) (3)

too trop (3)

to travel voyager (g → ge) (1)

Tuesday mardi (0)

twelve douze (0)

twenty vingt (0)

twenty-eight vingt-huit (0)

twenty-five vingt-cinq (0)

twenty-four vingt-quatre (0)

twenty-nine vingt-neuf (0)

twenty-one vingt et un (0)

twenty-seven vingt-sept (0)

twenty-six vingt-six (0)

twenty-three vingt-trois (0)

twenty-two vingt-deux (0)

two deux (0)

uncle l'oncle (3)

to use utiliser (2)

vegetarian végétarien/végétarienne (1)

Vietnamese vietnamien/vietnamienne (1)

the Vietnamese language le vietnamien (1)

visual arts les arts (m. pl.) visuels (2)

volunteer bénévole (1)

to watch a show/film regarder une série/un film (1)

Wednesday mercredi (0)

week la semaine (2)

weekend le week-end (2)

WC les toilettes (f. pl.) (3)

What? Que/qu'? (1)

What do you like to study? Qu'est-ce que tu aimes étudier? (1)

What is the date? Quelle est la date? (0, 1)

What time is it? Quelle heure est-il? (2)

What's your name? Comment t'appelles-tu? (0, 1)

When? Quand? (1)

When is your birthday? C'est quand ton anniversaire? (0, 1)

Where?/From where? Où?/D'où? (1)

Where do you come from? D'où viens-tu? (0, 1)

Which? What? Quel(le)? (1)

Which languages do you speak? Quelles langues est-ce que parles? (1)

whiteboard le tableau (2)

Who? Qui? (1)

Who am I? Qui suis-je? (1)

Who is your teacher? Qui est ton professeur? (1)

Why? Pourquoi? (1)

Why do you study French? Pourquoi est-ce que tu étudies le français? (1)

to work travailler (1)

to work in teams travailler en équipe (2)

to work in the office travailler au bureau (2)

to write écrire (1)

young jeune (3)

Expressions utiles English-French

always toujours (3)

during the week pendant la semaine (2)

during the weekend pendant le week-end (2)

first conversations les premières conversations (0)

go back to your seats retournez à vos places (0)

I'm from... Je viens de... (0)

I don't have a lot of... Je n'ai pas beaucoup de/d'... (2)

I don't know! Je ne sais pas! (3)

I don't need... J'ai besoin de/d'... (2)

I have a lot of... J'ai beaucoup de/d'... (2)

I know! Je sais! (3)

I need... J'ai besoin de/d'... (2)

It's month + number C'est le + numéro + mois (0)

Me neither! Moi non plus! (1)

Me too! Moi aussi! (1)

often souvent (3)

Ok! D'accord! (3)

rarely rarement (3)

rather assez (3)

really vraiment (3)

Really cool! Vachement cool! (3)

so si (3)

That's awesome! C'est génial! (3)

That's great! C'est super! (1)

That's interesting! C'est intéressant! (1)

There is/are... Il y a (2)

too trop (3)

Very good! Très bien! (1)

you need... il vous faut... (0)

Credits

Every effort has been made to determine the copyright owners. In case of any omissions, the publisher will be happy to make suitable acknowledgements in future editions. All credits are listed in the order of appearance.

All images are © Shutterstock and © Thinkstock, except as noted below. Cover image: Andriy Kravchenko / Alamy Stock Photo

Unité préliminaire

© Miniwatts Marketing Group, "Top Ten Languages in the Internet in millions of users - June 2016", Retrieved from http://www.internetworldstats.com/stats7.htm. 2017.

© Wikipedia, "Liste de Pays ayant le français comme langue officielle" CC BY-SA 3.0, https://creativecommons. org/licenses/by-sa/3.0/legalcode, Retrieved from https:// en.wikipedia.org/wiki/List_of_territorial_entities_where_ French_is_an_official_language. 2018.

© Bamse, "Pays ayant le français comme langue officielle", CC BY-SA 3.0, https://creativecommons.org/licenses/by-sa/3.0/legalcode, Retrieved from https://commons.wikimedia. org/wiki/File:French_official_language_world_map.svg. 2007.

© Marc Degioanni - Conseiller pédagogique - Digne, "Monde 4 Francophonie", Retrieved from © Babsy, "Carte des indicatifs téléphoniques français", CC BY 3.0, https:// creativecommons.org/licenses/by/3.0/, Retrieved from https:// en.wikipedia.org/wiki/Telephone_numbers_in_France#/ media/File:Carte_indicatifs_t%C3%A9l%C3%A9phoniques_ fran%C3%A7ais.svg. 2008.

© Centre de vacances des Alpes, "Séjours été 2017", Retrieved from http://www.cvalpes.fr/camps-colonies-ete/. 2017.

© Telligo, "Les séjours", Recreated from http://www.telligo. fr. 2017.

Images Unité préliminaire

p. 3 (Photo), © Marianne*. 2018.

p. 3 (Photo), © Noah*. 2018.

p. 3 (Photo), © Jeanne*. 2018.

p. 3 (Photo), © François*. 2018.

p. 3 (Photo), © Hamid*. 2018.

p. 3 (Photo), © Kate*. 2018.

p. 3 (Photo), © Arianne*. 2018.

p.10 (Michelin Man), ©Michelin, Michelin Man photo provided by Michelin North America Branding and Heritage.

p. 26 (image, Léopold Sédar Senghor), © Egon Steiner (Original), RoyFocker 12 (Derivative work) "Frankfurt/ Main, Staatspräsident von Senegal, Léopold Sédar Senghor", CC BY-SA 3.0, https://creativecommons.org/

licenses/by-sa/3.0/legalcode, Retrieved from https:// commons.wikimedia.org/w/index.php?curid=6826849.

p. 26 (image, Edith Piaf), © Eric Koch, "Edith Piaf 914-6440. jpg", CC BY-SA 3.0 NL, https://creativecommons.org/licenses/ by-sa/3.0/nl/deed.en, Retrieved from https://commons. wikimedia.org/w/index.php?curid=21003436. 2016.

p. 27 (fêtes de Bayonne 1997), © Ville de Bayonne, "Fêtes de Bayonne 1997", Retrieved from http://www.fetes.bayonne.fr/ photos/329-les-affiches-des-fetes/2.html. 1997.

p. 29 (Painting of a group of musicians during Fêtes de Bayonne), © Patrick Larcebal, "Aux Fêtes de Bayonne un festival de bérets rouges et … non de bonnets !", used with permission.

p. 32 (image, Bénabar), © Georges Biard, "Bénabar 2012", CC BY-SA 3.0, https://creativecommons.org/licenses/by-sa/3.0/deed.en, Retrieved from https://commons.wikimedia. org/w/index.php?curid=18608347. 2012.

p. 33 (image, Laurent Voulzy), © Remi Jouan, "Voulzy Concert Belle-Ile (2).jpg", CC BY-SA 3.0, https://creativecommons. org/licenses/by-sa/3.0/deed.en, Retrieved from https:// commons.wikimedia.org/w/index.php?curid=1877781. 2007.

p. 33 (image, Camille), © daniel - originally posted to Flickr as Camille, live in Melbourne, "Camille 20090121 Melbourne 1.jpg", CC BY 2.0, https://creativecommons.org/ licenses/by/2.0/deed.en, Retrieved from https://commons. wikimedia.org/w/index.php?curid=9811157. 2009.

Unité 1

© Qyd, "Map of Quebec", Public Domain, Retrieved from https://commons.wikimedia.org/wiki/File:QC-Canada-province.png. 2006.

© Touristmaker, "What are the largest French-speaking cities in the world?", Information retrieved from http:// www.touristmaker.com/blog/what-are-the-largest-french-speaking-cities-in-the-world/. 2017.

© Wikipedia, "Liste des destinations touristiques mondiales", CC BY-SA 3.0, https://creativecommons. org/licenses/by-sa/3.0/deed.fr, Retrieved from https:// fr.wikipedia.org/wiki/Liste_des_destinations_touristiques_ mondiales. 2017.

© Wikipedia, "France", CC BY-SA 3.0, https://en.wikipedia. org/wiki/Wikipedia:Text_of_Creative_Commons_

---

*To protect the privacy of these generous French speakers, we have changed or omitted their last names.

Attribution-ShareAlike_3.0_Unported_License, Information retrieved from https://en.wikipedia.org/wiki/France. 2017.

© Justin Trudeau, "Meet Justin Trudeau", Information retrieved from https://www.liberal.ca/rt-hon-justin-trudeau. 2017.

© Wikipedia, "Handball at the Summer Olympics", CC BY-SA 3.0, https://creativecommons.org/licenses/by-sa/3.0/legalcode, Retrieved from https://en.wikipedia.org/wiki/Handball_at_the_Summer_Olympics.

© Sofinscope, "Les 10 principaux loisirs des Français", Recreated from http://www.offremedia.com/le-budget-loisirs-des-francais-progresse-de-11-en-2015-selon-le-barometre-sofinscope. 2015.

© Toussaint 2017 – Hiver & printemps 2018, "Apprendre en s'amusant, Saint-Yrieix-la-Perche SPORT ACADEMY", Retrieved from https://www.action-sejours.com/14732_AS_CATAL_Hiver2017_printemps_2018.pdf, p. 38. 2017-2018.

© Festival d'été de Québec, "FEQ", Retrieved from https://www.infofestival.com/Programmation/Affiche. 2018.

© Med Poly School, "Cours des Langues", Recreated from http://www.sfax-annonce.com/Produits/22014-05-09-11-08-3350621.langue.jpg?PHPSESSID=2e8c2707c927f7fe9146046039 96a6a5. 2014.

© Statistics Canada, "Population by knowledge of official language, by province and territory (2011 Census)", Data retrieved from http://www.statcan.gc.ca/tables-tableaux/sum-som/l01/cst01/demo15-eng.htm. 2013.

© European Commission, "Eurobaromètre spécial 386", Information retrieved from http://ec.europa.eu/commfrontoffice/publicopinion/archives/ebs/ebs_386_fr.pdf, p.17. 2012.

© "Perspective culturelle: L'identité linguistique du Québec", Information retrieved from http://www.linternaute.com/histoire/motcle/94/a/1/1/quebec.shtml. 2018.

© "Perspective culturelle: L'identité linguistique du Québec", Information retrieved from https://www.republiquelibre.org/couture/EXPRES.HTM. 1996.

Images Unité 1

pp. 42, 44 (Photo), © Marianne*. 2018.

pp. 43, 44 (Photo), © François*. 2018.

p. 42 (License Plate, Québec), © Gachepi, "Plaque immatriculation Québec", CC BY-SA 3.0, https://creativecommons.org/licenses/by-sa/3.0/legalcode, Retrieved from https://commons.wikimedia.org/wiki/File:Plaque_immatriculation_Québec.JPG. 2007.

p. 42 (image, Samuel de Champlain), © Théophile Hamel, "Samuel-de-champlain-s.jpg", CC BY-SA 3.0, https://creativecommons.org/licenses/by-sa/3.0/, Retrieved from https://commons.wikimedia.org/w/index.php?curid=525161. 2010.

p. 43 (image, Jacques Cousteau), © Peters, Hans / Anefo, "Cousteau1972 (cropped).jpg", CC BY-SA 3.0, https://creativecommons.org/licenses/by-sa/3.0/deed.en, Retrieved from https://commons.wikimedia.org/w/index.php?curid=33519331. 2016.

p. 43 (Coco Chanel red dress) Lebrecht Music & Arts / Alamy Stock Photo

Unité 2

© Wikimedia Commons, "Algeria Map", Public Domain, Retrieved from https://commons.wikimedia.org/w/index.php?curid=165633. 2005.

© OpenStreetMap Contributors, "Location Map Algiers", pinpoint for El Macir added, CC BY-SA 2.0, https://creativecommons.org/licenses/by-sa/2.0/legalcode, www.openstreetmap.org/copyright, Retrieved from https://commons.wikimedia.org/w/index.php?curid=16706308. 2005.

© The American International School of Algiers, "Home Page", Retrieved from https://www.aisalgiers.org/. 2017.

© Ministère de l'Éducation Nationale, "À chaque classe son emploi du temps", Retrieved from http://www.education.gouv.fr/cid80/les-horaires-par-cycle-au-college.html. 2017.

© Ministère de l'Éducation Nationale, "The French Digital Plan for Education", Retrieved from http://cache.media.education.gouv.fr/file/01_-_janvier/88/1/The_French_Digital_Plan_For_Education_527881.pdf. 2015.

© Les Bourgeons, "Home Page", Retrieved from http://lesbourgeons.net/. 2017.

© Lycée International Alexandre Dumas Alger, "Home Page", Retrieved from http://www.liad-alger.fr/joomla/. 2017.

© Ministère de l'Éducation Nationale de la République Algérienne Démocratique et Populaire, "Sujets et corrigés des examens officiels", Retrieved from http://www.education.gov.dz/fr/sujets-et-corriges-des-examens-officiels/. 2017.

Images Unité 2

pp. 90, 92 (Photo), © Hamid*. 2018.

p. 94 (Cahiers, Image of different color notebooks), © Clairefontaine, "Cahier, carnets et blocs", Adapted from https://www.clairefontaine.com/produit-fr-3120c-cahier-pique-21x297-80p-uni.html.

p. 110 (Photos), © Jean Coibion. 2017.

Unité 3

© Pierre Lozère (music) and Bernard François (lyrics), with the permission of Éditions Marypierre, "Toute la famille", Retrieved from www.papaclown.com. 1983.

© Iweps, "Répartition des ménages privés wallons selon le type au 1er janvier 2017 (en pourcentage)", Retrieved from https://www.iweps.be/indicateur-statistique/nombre-et-taille-des-menages/. 2017.

© Centre d'observation de la société, "Dans quel type de famille vivent les enfants?", Retrieved from http://www.observationsociete.fr/structures-familiales/familles/de-plus-en-plus-de-familles-recomposees.html. 2017.

© Rcragun, "Types of U.S. Households, 2002", CC BY 3.0, https://creativecommons.org/licenses/by/3.0/legalcode, Retrieved from https://commons.wikimedia.org/w/index.php?curid=8390557. 2009.

Images Unité 3

Thanks to Maria, for always getting me out of trouble.
To Xulia, for your unconditional support, and to you, Germ.

NÚRIA TAMARIT

DAUGHTERS OF SNOW AND CINDERS

TRANSLATED BY JENNA ALLEN

**Helen Plum Library
Lombard, IL**

FANTAGRAPHICS 🔥 SEATTLE • WA

Your realm and mine are utterly different.

Thousands of miles separate them.

But, even today, despite the distance that separates us...

We share the same enemies.

Here, quick!

Whoa! We've saved one sack at least.

Is it full?

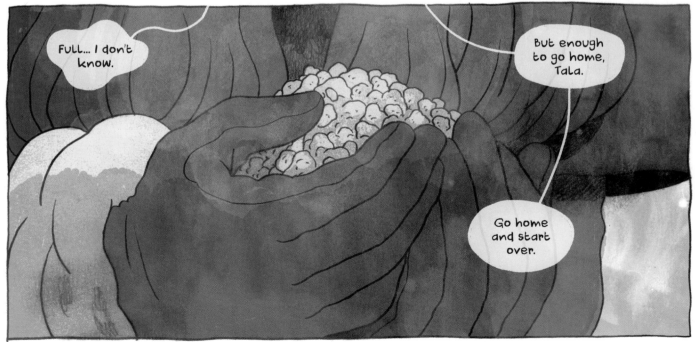

Full... I don't know.

But enough to go home, Tala.

Go home and start over.

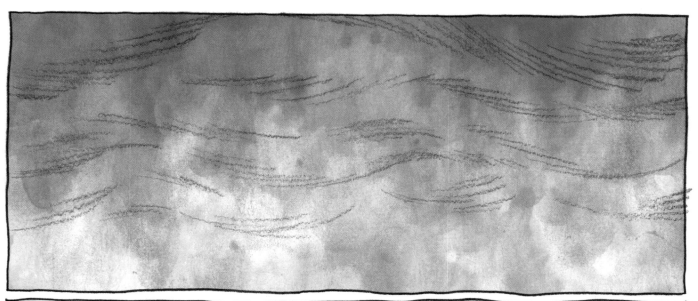

Joana, you know if they search us and find all this gold, they won't let us leave here.

Since we're women, they'll say we stole it.

Well, we did steal it, didn't we?

PART ONE

DEPARTURE

Some time ago,
I heard about El Dorado.

Crowds of men traveled there. They
said that once you got there, you
could join a gold panning expedition.

And it would only
take a few weeks
or months for you...

...to return home,
rich beyond imagining.

At that moment, I thought
I had nowhere to go,
no home.

It was worth a shot.

I sold my few possessions.
It was just enough to buy a ticket.

OK, first things first: find some gear and provisions.

Thank you.

Just look how nice this skin is, it's a good deal!

Fine, I'll trade you for the snowshoes.

Your blanket for my gun, final offer.

Done!

ALL ready for adventure...

SLAM!

Your math is wrong, AGAIN! That ain't right!

What're ya tryin' to pull?

Pardon me, can I please sign up for...

...the next expedition, if possible.

Pssh...

Where'd SHE come from?!

No women!

What would you do with gold, anyway?!

None of your beeswax.

Pff... go on, beat it!

My pleasure!

See ya!

What's she doing? She won't last long like that...

Lousy jerks.

Pssst

Looking for an expedition?

AH!

13

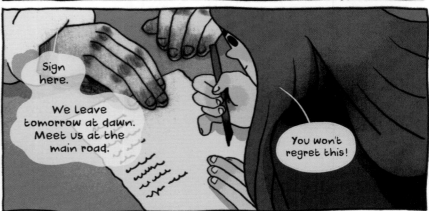

14

15

I can't believe those jerks!

Hey, "healer," pick up the pace!

We've just set off and she's already slowin' us down!

I warned Matwei this would happen!

She was the only doctor available...

That redskin, a doctor?! More like a witch!

Opa, you have to walk faster.

If you become a burden...

...we'll leave you behind!

I'm doing my best, Semiov.

KYAH

18

19

Oh my God!

HEH

HEH

HEH

Damn dogs.

That's how you teach 'em: with the rod.

Monster.

You're all messed up...

You can't stay like this.

I'm sorry.

You're not going to like this.

23

24

25

SHHHH

ARF
ARF
ARF

See, these are moose tracks.

Looks like he's heading north...

How'd he disappear so quickly?

His tracks are clearer here.

Let's go!

We'll get 'im!

27

When I think about it, I tell myself the enemy was always among us.

TOK TOK TOK TOK

We sat at the same table.

We slept in the same bed.

But that was nothing compared to what I would later learn.

All considered, my childhood was pretty sheltered.

Until the day my grandmother told me what it meant to be a woman...

...and that I must never trust men.

SLUP SLUP SLUP

Hey! What're you doing?

You keep holding us up!

C'mere, I'll change your bandage.

After several days, I had only one thing on my mind: food.

33

34

Mmm... Not bad!

Here's your share. You've earned it!

I'd give anything to taste her food again...

...my grandmother's recipes, that she learned from her mother, and her mother learned from hers, and so on all the way back.

She taught me the name of every plant and every animal that lived in our realm.

To treat Nature with benevolence and to take only what's needed.

To love Nature like a mother, a sister!

Later I learned that some people did not cherish Nature. They hurt her, even.

38

Hold up!

Shhh

Quiet.

HA HA HA HA HA HA HA

I don't trust that Tala girl...

In the village, they said she was the best guide.

Me neither. How'd she find us? She sniffed us out like a dog!

Yeah, and a woman to boot, that's all we need!

This way.

We'll camp a little ways away.

We'll wait for sunrise. I don't have the courage to face them tonight.

You've proven that you're up to the task...

...and that you're a superb tracker.

I'm counting on you to lead us safely through.

And I warn you to not try anything funny.

Cos if I don't get any gold...

...you won't get enough air to breathe.

I know, Matwei.

And I know where I'm going, this land is my home.

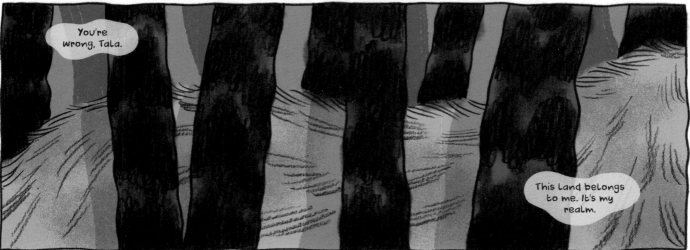

You're wrong, Tala.

This land belongs to me. It's my realm.

Hello, everyone...

How's rabbit sound for breakfast?

Well.

Well.

Well.

In exchange, let me join you.

You said she wouldn't follow us!

Should we kill her?

I wouldn't advise that... I won't go down easy.

If you don't want me, then give me some food and I'll be on my way.

You're not going anywhere, you loon.

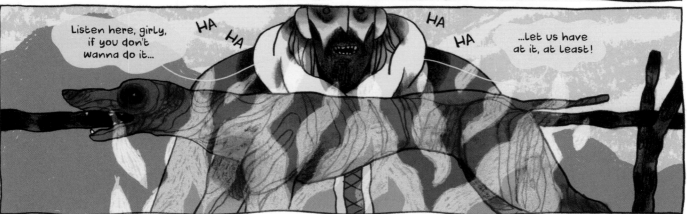

43

PART TWO

SWIMMING UPSTREAM

I'll stay on my path, alone.

Not a single animal to shoot for miles.

Our meager stocks won't be enough...

Here, enjoy it. I don't know when we'll eat again.

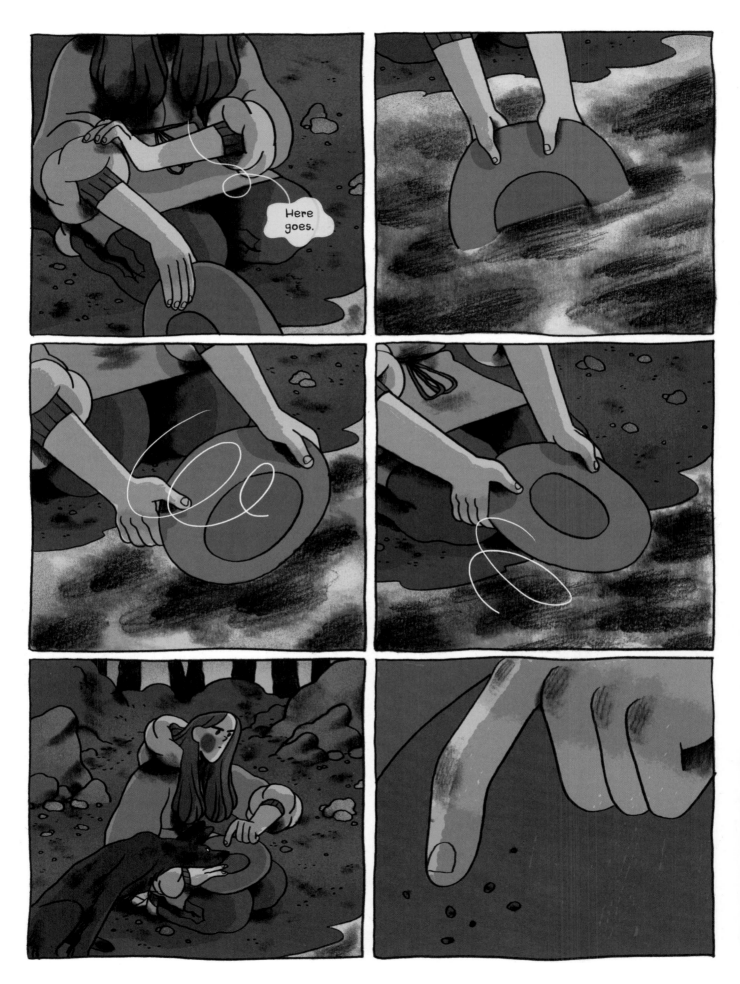

54

55

After a few days of fruitless searching in the sediment of the river, a new thought slowly came to me...

Back home, "wealth" wasn't the worth of a golden metal.

It was something else.

It was the golden color of the sun...

...or maize, lemon, quince...

57

For just a moment, I was home again, happy and carefree.

Sadly, I woke up.
It was just a dream.

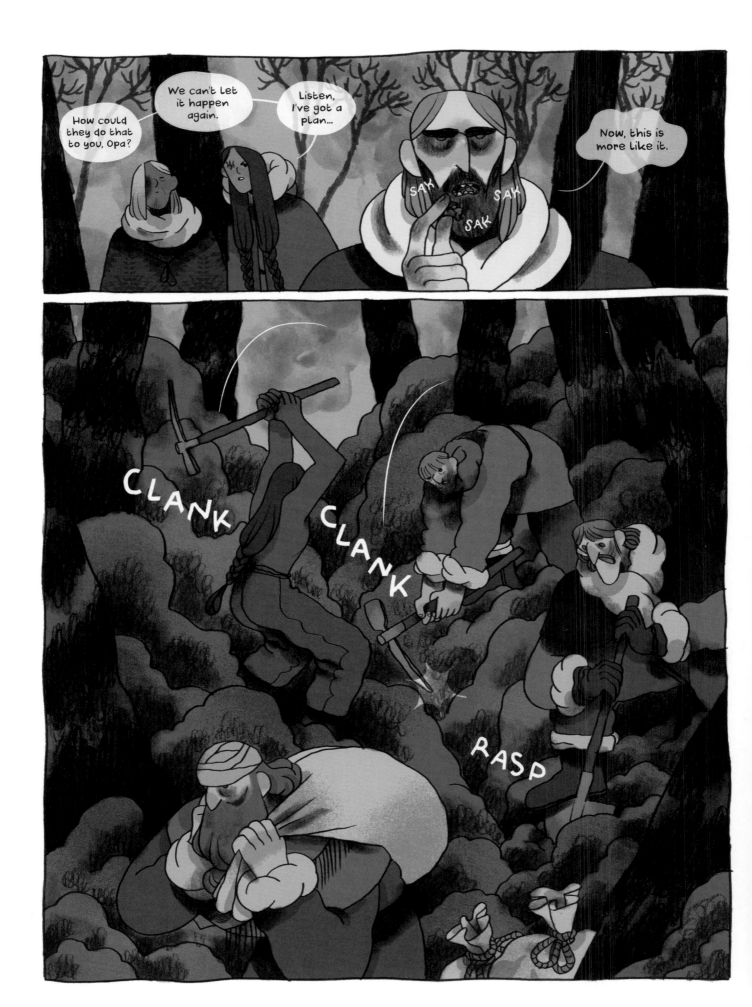

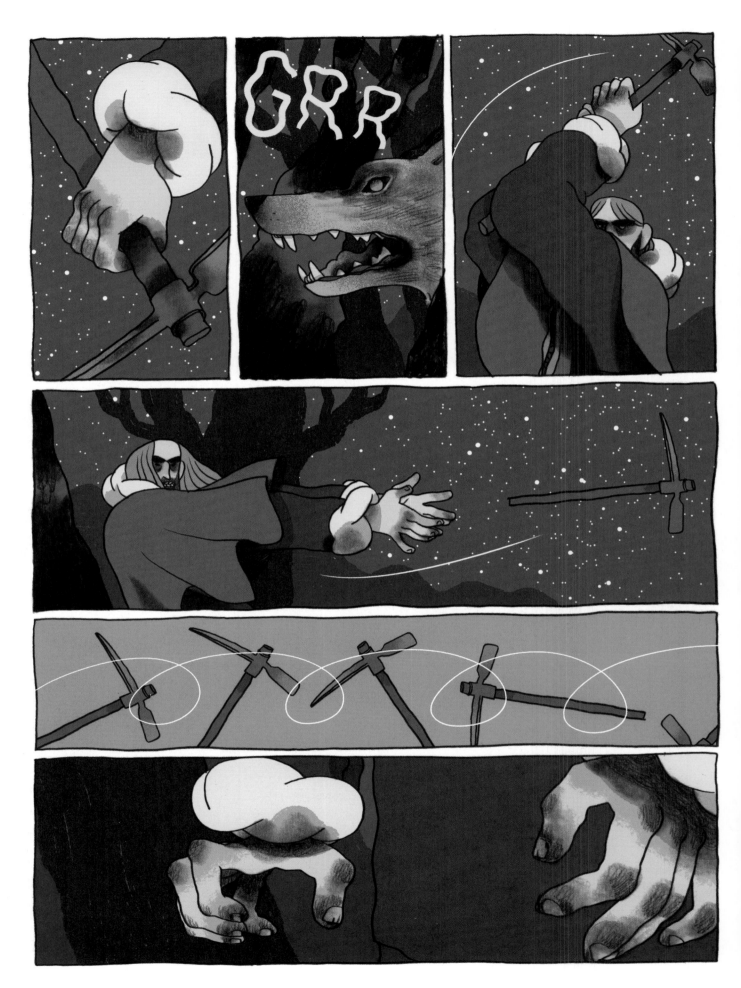

I'm seeking gold too.

But I didn't really have a choice.

Was I better than them?

I believe, back then...

...I wasn't ready to face the truth yet.

Agh! Is there nothing left to hunt?!

We'll need to keep tightening our belts.

Winter is already here and I only have a single nugget of gold.

GRRL

Let's cozy up.

You're so warm, Peg.

It felt good to hold someone in my arms.

To feel
a body's
warmth...

82

I was wrong to doubt you, Tala!

Who'd've thought! A woman's made me rich!

HA HA

HA

KYAH

85

It's dumping snow!

We'll need to find shelter.

And we'll have the chance to eat a bit.

Oh geez, these tracks are really fresh. Let's hope they're not Matwei's.

I would've liked to never leave.

To end my days there and admire the fields forever.

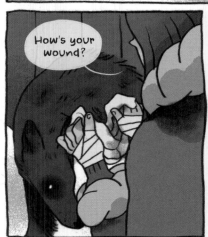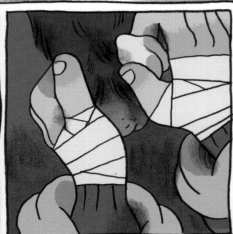

OK, there's no chance he'll come now.

I had never seen such colors before.

The snow...

...blood...

...gold...

...here, even the colors of night were different.

PART THREE

GRAY FLESH

After two days and nights, we continued on our way.

What riches does this river hold?

This might be our last chance, Peg.

If I don't find anything, it's over. We'll have to go back to the village and try again next season.

SPLASH

WHOA!

What was that? A fish?

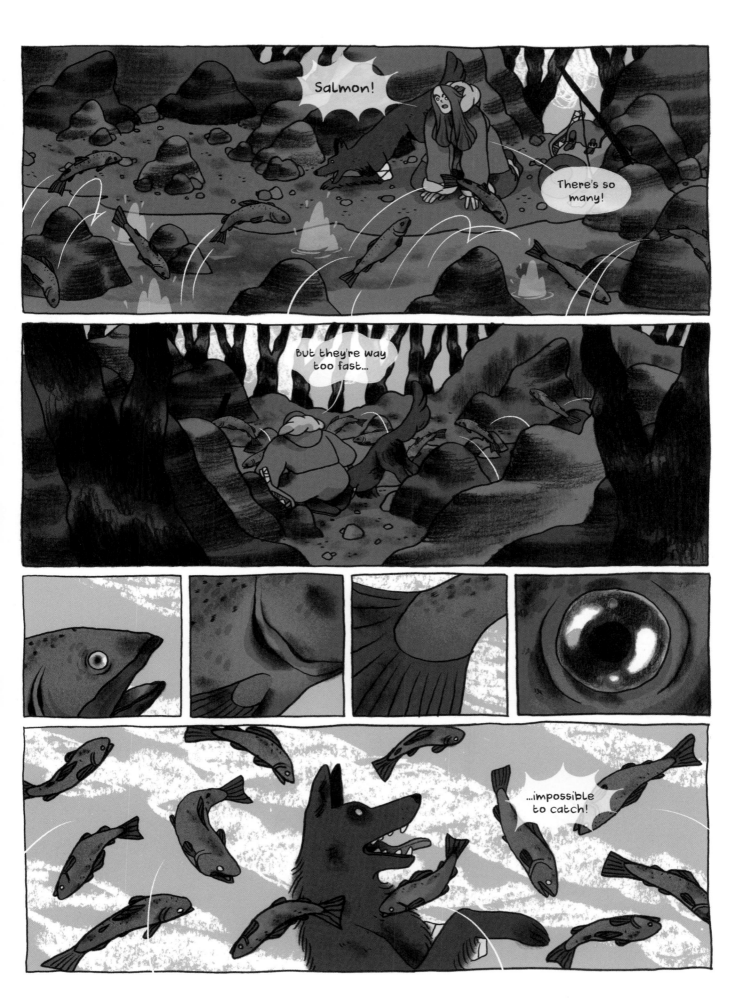

Salmon!

There's so many!

But they're way too fast...

...impossible to catch!

Let me think...

Agh! Nothing to make a fishing pole with.

How about an old-fashioned harpoon...

This branch'll do the trick!

OK, Joana, concentrate!

103

Look, some have stunned themselves crashing into the rocks!

You know what that means?!

Ha ha

Ha ha

We're gonna have a feast!

It's not going so bad now, is it, my friend?

I think you're my lucky charm.

We only hunted what we needed.

We harvested
what we needed.

And Nature gave us back
a hundred times what we took.

I believe my grandmother loved her land more than my grandfather and that she wanted to pass that unconditional love on to me.

I feel like this land is mine.

You have to take care of it and cultivate it, because it belongs to you too.

But it's not your property.

The land belongs to you because it's part of you.

Because it IS you.

The land is me?

Yes, wholly.

PEE-YOO!

All these dead salmon!

Such a bummer!

We can't take them all or eat them all!

I didn't know if they were still edible. The last thing I needed was to get sick out here.

What a waste.

110

Let's see if we can salvage something.

Rss Rss

Huh, the flesh is all gray.

I've never seen a fish that looks like this before...

It doesn't smell bad...

...but I'm not sure if we can eat it.

Too bad.

C'mon, let's go, Peg.

115

So, have you found gold?

No.

And has Matwei found all that he wanted?

Matwei, like all men from here, would let himself be put in chains if they were made of gold.

So no, not as much as he would like.

Well, it's too bad he's not in chains!

It's frozen already.

CLON

CLON

CRAK

116

KYAH

I'm afraid Semiov's found me.

Who's Semiov?

Matwei's right-hand man.

He was born here, like me.

He knows this land very well, and he's owed Matwei a debt for a very long time.

When Semiov was young, he was attacked by a wolf and lost his eye.

Matwei killed the wolf and saved his life.

So Semiov thinks that he owes Matwei everything.

That he must serve Matwei forever.

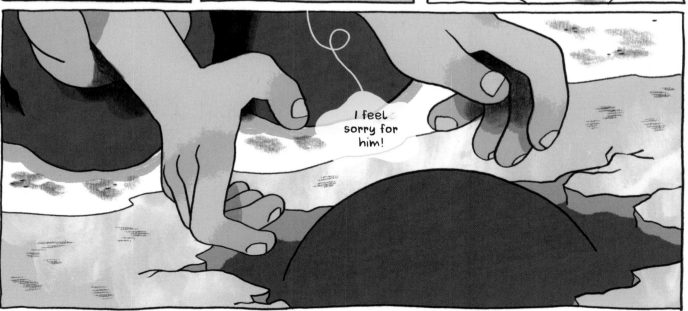

I feel sorry for him!

118

BRRom

BRRooom

A storm started to roll in, and we went in search of shelter. It was a matter of life or death.

Opa was a very quiet companion.

Like an animal you can barely hear walking behind you.

Opa was starting to intrigue me...

I wanted to learn more about her and this land...

Without really talking about it, we decided to make the cabin habitable so we could stay until the storm passed...

This house almost felt like our home.

Opa, look! This one's still edible too!

As those few days passed in the cabin, I learned to trust Opa.

It's not like I had anyone else.

But...
What did
Matwei do?

He
watched.

That's the
whole story.

That's the
true nature
of men in
our world.

The fire is low.
You should fetch
more wood.

I'm
so sorry,
Opa.

It's not
your fault.
Go on.

I'll come
right back.

OK.

I'm taking
my rifle in
case I see
any game.

Opa never spoke of it again.

I don't know if it pained her. I never saw her tending her wound.

Sometimes, she stared into the distance, as if she were observing something I couldn't see.

No way, we're out of wood again.

HAHAHA

HEY, LOOK!

LOOK WHAT WE GOT HERE!

MATWEI!

Nooo! Opa's still inside!

133

134

ZZZZ

CLAP! ZZZZ

Those roots Opa told me about did the trick!

They should sleep until tomorrow evening!

Hang on, I recognize this fabric. It's Opa's scarf... She can't be far off!

With no shelter, no gold, almost no food, and no hope...

...I started to slide into despair.

I spent my time listening carefully...

...awaiting footfalls, the slightest breath.

Opa slept soundly, as if nothing troubled her.

What if Tala doesn't come, huh?

We've got to keep going.

Settle down, she'll come.

Hello.

Can I come in? A little warmth would do me good!

As soon as Tala joined us, the dynamics of the group totally changed.

There's one thing I don't understand.

Why didn't you two run away together?

Because Matwei would have followed us for sure.

He'd hunt us down.

Opa wasn't as important to him.

That's why she left first. To buy time and find you.

There was no way we'd let you go it alone. You don't know this land like we do.

Those men are monsters. We'd rather risk our lives than stay with them.

A few weeks into the expedition...

...we knew we had to escape, and rid the world of these men.

So I made them take the longest path...

...in the hopes that they wouldn't survive the winter.

But winter has trapped us too!

Your plan is suicidal.

No, I know a shortcut.

Ever since men like Matwei infested this continent long ago, they've exploited the land and destroyed it, day after day.

What was once our home, the land of our birth, no longer exists.

But it feels like you're different.

You don't view the land like they do.

So Tala and I decided that you too must survive.

What would we have left, if we didn't look after each other?

You're brave and strong. You proved that by making it this far all by yourself.

We can finish the journey together. Help each other.

Well, thanks.

I'll stay
with you.

Wonderful.
We'll all stick
together.

Brrr...

I'll go get
more wood.

Keep your ears
open. You never
know when...

Don't worry!
If we hear a falcon,
we'll take off!

143

Usually, you can hear everything from the mountaintop. But strangely, that night, I didn't hear a thing.

They must have been soldiers returning from war, looking for trouble.

Just passing through, and we were there.

They wanted to destroy us.

Just to satisfy their basest instincts. They killed...

...for the pleasure of it.

It was the smell of smoke that woke me, and I rushed down the mountain as fast as I could.

I saw the geraniums burning, bidding me farewell, like a last dance.

I ran as fast as I could, but when I arrived, it was all gone.

151

I felt like I was surrounded by people like me, in harmony, like never before.

What we were about to do was definitely crazy, but there was no going back.

156

Mmm...

It's cold.

Which one of you morons left the door open?

Matwei...

Someone stole some of our gold and provisions.

MY GOLD!

I'LL KILL WHOEVER DID THIS WITH MY BARE HANDS!

GET UP!

FIND ME THAT THIEF!

PART FOUR

OUR HOME

I know it's Tala. She might even be with Opa.

The size of the tracks means it's women. Probably three.

The third one might be the girl with the birthmark on her face.

Tala must think I don't know how to return to the village without her.

HA! I know exactly where we are.

That's Canderes Mountain over there, so we're about five days from home.

Am I right, Semiov?

You know this area too, don't you?

I'm sorry, Matwei...

...but that's Black Thunder Mountain. We're very far from the village.

WHAT? HOW FAR?

Three weeks.

And you knew this, all along?

No.
I only know the major landmarks in the area.

I didn't realize until now.

Tala fooled me too.

She took us on the longest trail. We thought we recognized the landscape.

We were oblivious.

Winter will catch us. She's led us to our deaths.

But if there was no way to get out of here alive, she wouldn't have left.

165

God, are you OK?

Are you hurt?

We have to get a head start to have any chance of shaking them.

We have to keep going!

But the falcon has already spotted us...

We're done for.

They're near, Matwei.

They're heading west.

We can still catch them.

Tell the men to get ready.

Quickly.

I'll go on ahead.

I'll move faster alone.

What're we gonna do? Opa has to rest.

If we stop here, we'll all...

Hello, ladies!

You women must be mad to leave the protection of men and run away!

And fools to think that you can steal from me and live!

170

171

Woof!

Woof!

C'mere!

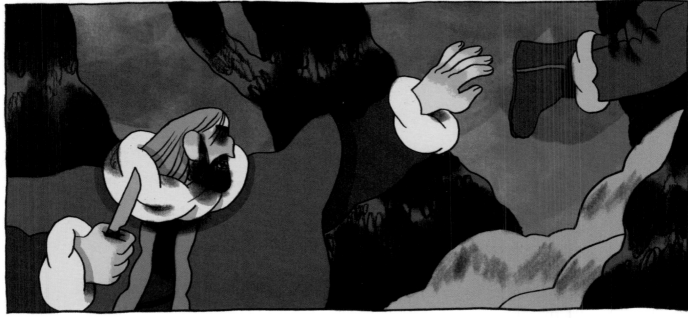

177

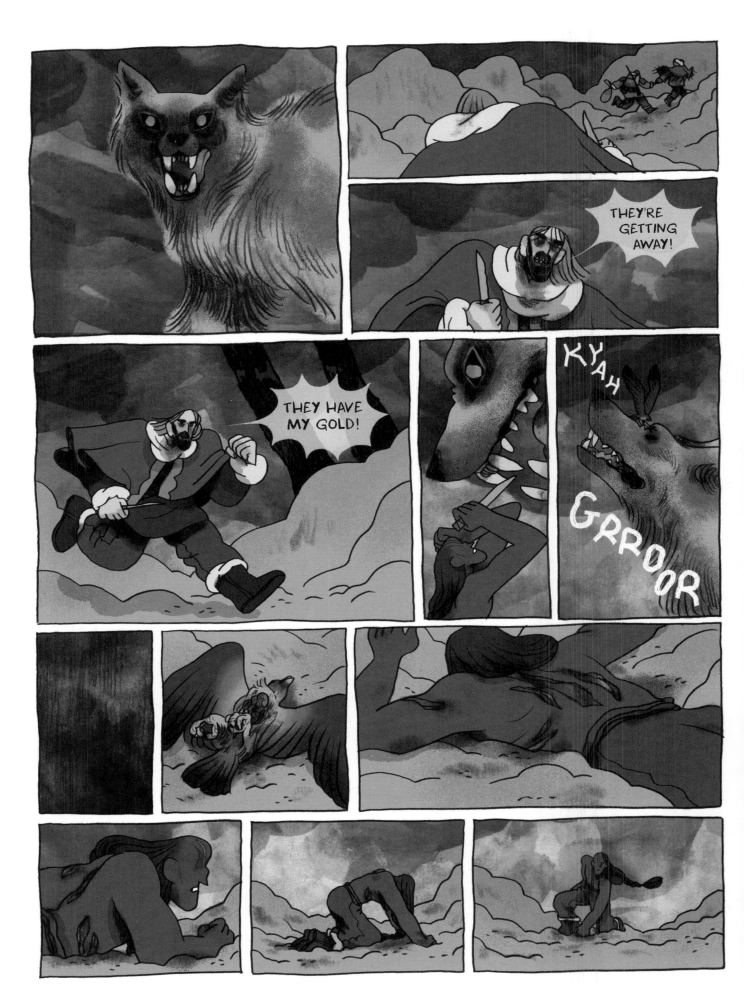

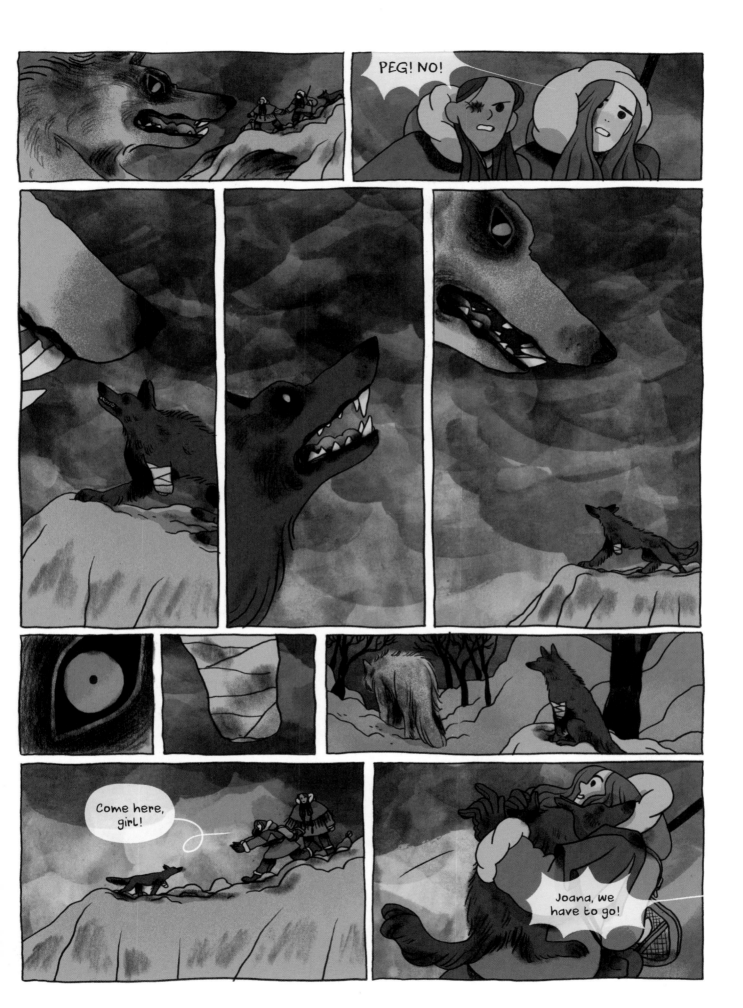

183

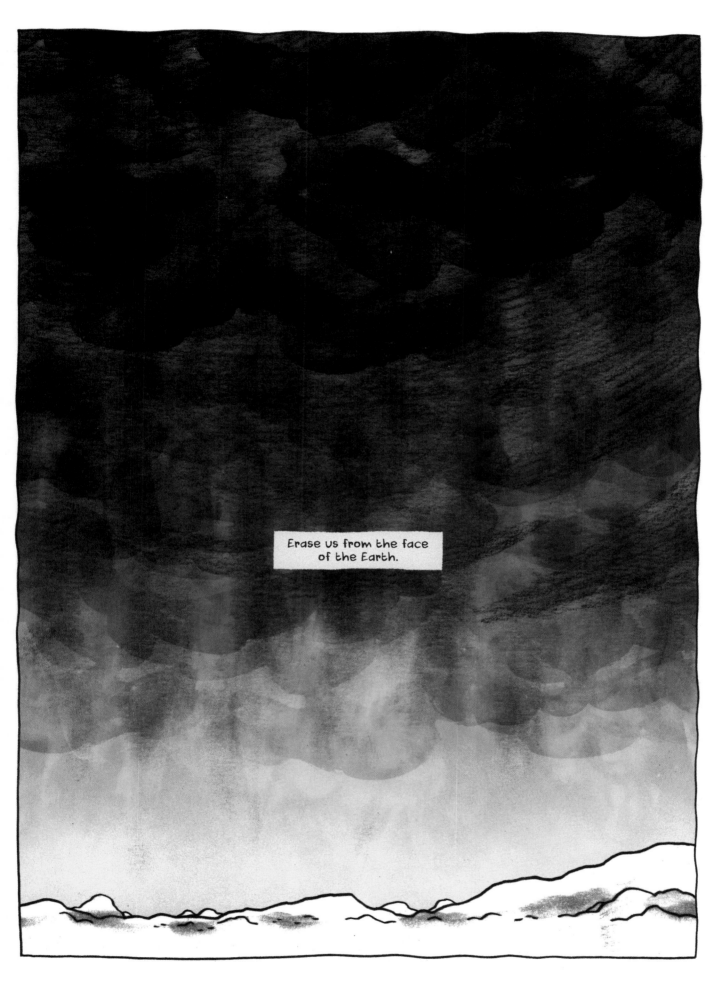

In the eye of the storm, I felt like, in a way, we had won a battle against our common enemy.

This time, I wouldn't be
the one losing it all.

I traveled across the ocean and, on behalf of all women, I defeated those men who had taken everything from us.

The men who wanted to make us believe we were worthless, and that they could exploit us, annihilate us, as they did to the land.

196

201

Stop right there!

No more games.

Give me the gold, now!

If I see you two again, you're dead.

205

You know what, Joana?

This might seem weird but...

...I feel like winter's offering us a truce.

Usually, at this time of year, we should be frozen and buried under the snow.

Maybe the land's forgiven us after all. Maybe...

...the land's letting me go home.

And you can stay with me, Tala, if you want.

ABOUT THE AUTHOR

Núria Tamarit is an illustrator and comic artist based in València, Spain. Her graphic world is marked by fantastical elements, voluptuous plant forms, dreamy creatures, and powerful female characters. Her previous books include *Season of the Witch* (2020, with Matt Ralphs) and *Giantess* (2022, with Jean-Christophe Deveney).

ABOUT THE TRANSLATOR

Jenna Allen is a freelance translator based in Colorado.

Translator: Jenna Allen
Editor: Conrad Groth
Designer: Justin Allan-Spencer
Production: C Hwang
Publicity: Jacq Cohen
VP / Associate Publisher: Eric Reynolds
President / Publisher: Gary Groth

Fantagraphics Books, Inc.
7563 Lake City Way NE
Seattle, WA 98115
www.fantagraphics.com
@fantagraphics

ISBN: 978-1-68396-756-9
Library of Congress Control Number: 2022949230
First Fantagraphics Books edition: Summer 2023
Printed in China

3 1502 00917 5827